WILLIAMSBURG REPRODUCTIONS

W.

$\mathcal{B}$RICK *and wood combine with* Williamsburg *reproductions to create a serene living room. Floral Bough covers a CW 129 Sofa, and a rich silk damask the CW 128 Chair. A CW 8 Tea Table is charming in this warm room, and* Williamsburg *fireplace accessories, brass candlesticks, and glass decanters decorate the fireplace area.*

Williamsburg®

REPRODUCTIONS

❖

Interior Designs for Today's Living

❖

Craft House

WILLIAMSBURG, VIRGINIA

WILLIAMSBURG RESTORATION, INCORPORATED

WILLIAMSBURG, VIRGINIA 23185

Copyright 1965, Williamsburg Restoration, Incorporated

Williamsburg and the Hallmark are registered trademarks of

Williamsburg Restoration, Incorporated

January, 1969

The Wren Building

The Governor's Palace

Bruton Parish Church

The Capitol

Duke of Gloucester Street

The careful town plan of eighteenth-century Williamsburg is clear in this detailed map drawn by a French billeting officer in 1782. The Wren building, intellectual center of the College of William and Mary, and the Capitol, site of twice-yearly legislative deliberations, stood at either end of mile-long Duke of Gloucester Street. In the center of the town the Governor's Palace and Bruton Parish Church dominated the landscape.

The Williamsburg Tradition

WILLIAMSBURG's Duke of Gloucester Street has been described as "the most beautiful mile in American history." It was not by accident that it won such acclaim.

Since 1699, when it became one of the first planned towns in America, Williamsburg has been a tribute to design, order, and tasteful surroundings. Its early citizens and its twentieth-century restorers have been moved by its master plan, and today, even a casual passage through the Historic Area becomes a memorable experience, crowded with thousands of glimpses of well-rendered design.

When Governor Francis Nicholson drew his notable Williamsburg plan his objects were utilitarian, though his landscape was beautiful: space and serenity and trees and open greens and gardens surrounded the houses. The buildings themselves were built to rigid specifications (to a minimum of 20 by 30 feet on the Duke of Gloucester Street, on lots of at least half an acre).

Though the layout of the streets was as old as Pericles, the open axis of Market Square and Palace Green was an innovation of the sort that has kept the town plan fresh and beautiful for more than two centuries. It was about this carefully prescribed town plan that the Williamsburg traditions of taste and

The harmony of texture, line, and shape is a source of unexpected delight in the architecture and interiors of Williamsburg buildings. The pattern of a lantern's reflection, the rhythm of turns in a stairway or chimney, and the repetition of designs in different forms — for instance the Capitol's cone roof suddenly reappears in its gate finial — all contribute to Williamsburg's visual unity.

5

good living grew up. They were British in origin and feel, just as British taste had been adapted from Continental models, all with an ancestry tracing to Greece and Rome. In Williamsburg, there were charming Tidewater Virginia adaptations.

These were based on almost 100 years of life along the tidal rivers of the colony, shrewdly devised with an eye to the climate, the tobacco economy, the demands of crude transatlantic commerce, and the bounty of a virgin land where fine food was in plenty for all.

From this background, within sight of an elegant Governor's Palace and a striking Capitol on the fringe of the wilderness, and among a group of homes and taverns reminiscent of an English country town, the Virginia Way developed. It was soon to be seen in locally produced silver, pottery, brass, furniture, carriages, leather goods, and clothing. Usually, despite a common ancestry, these Virginia products differed from those of New England and Pennsylvania and other colonies. The difference seems to have been the influence of the tiny capital of Williamsburg, where patterns of taste were set.

The tastemakers of colonial Virginia were not always conscious artists of fashion; they often improvised. They did not hesitate to mix styles and centuries, nor to subordinate accepted vogues to the demands of daily use. But from the start, when the finest of imported furniture and furnishings appeared

Continuity of design is one other statement of the Williamsburg tradition. The individual motifs of railing, fence, and bench, though not the same, reflect a genius for unity of design.

in the parlors of Williamsburg, there was an awareness of a tasteful tradition, of a cultivated approach to life on the recent frontier.

Other small cities, in Virginia and out, were subjected to the same flow of ideas, and the common tastes of the passing generations. And yet, as is very clear today, the absence of a detailed plan of city development robbed these other towns of distinction. It is the heritage of conscious early planning that sets Williamsburg apart today, as always.

Not only does the scene of Williamsburg's restoration emphasize this heritage—beauty and appreciation of beauty are to be seen in chimneys, fence palings, blinds and eaves and window panes, in porch rails and hitching posts, garden walks, and finials on small outbuildings. Only professional architects aware of our history can note the reason: all Williamsburg structures, large and small, and even the gardens themselves, are based on geometric designs, faithfully carried out in detail.

It is a philosophy which can be carried into our life today. The effective use of proportion, detail, and symmetry that were essential to the tastemakers of 200 years ago continue as the key to harmonious surroundings.

Gardens, houses, streets, and rooms all reflect ideals of taste and design that are basic to the Williamsburg tradition. Grace of proportion and rhythm of pattern, honest use of materials, subtle harmony of varied designs: these ancient concepts are as applicable to today's living as they were to the towns and homes of two centuries ago.

REPRODUCTIONS PROGRAM

FROM its modest beginning in 1937, the Reproductions Program of Colonial Williamsburg has grown to include today more than 1,000 items of furniture, fabrics, wallpaper, paint, glass, ceramics, prints, crystal, silver, pewter, and brass. Each of these reproductions is a meticulous copy or adaptation of an antique in Colonial Williamsburg's restored buildings.

Guided by wills, inventories, and other records, the Department of Collections of Colonial Williamsburg has searched the world for antiques of the eighteenth century and earlier to furnish the Exhibition Buildings of this historic city. The furniture and accessories thus assembled reflect the taste and manners of the colonial Virginian, his desire for order and elegance on the edge of the wilderness. On the great plantations near Williamsburg he made his fortune in tobacco. The sailing ships that carried his yearly crop to England for sale returned laden with the "newest London fashion" in furniture, silver, glass, china, and fabrics. With these he furnished his riverside plantation and his Williamsburg home. Today in Colonial Williamsburg these homes, as well as a number of public buildings, have been restored to their original beauty after years of painstaking research into architecture, landscaping, and furnishings.

From the earliest days of the restoration, visitors to the historic city have been inspired by the grace and beauty of these colonial buildings and furnishings. In response to visitors' demands for furniture and accessories of equal quality for their own homes, Colonial Williamsburg began in 1937 a program of reproductions. Manufacturers who are in sympathy with the high standards required, and who have qualified craftsmen and facilities, have been licensed to make reproductions of these fine antiques under the supervision of Williamsburg Restoration, Incorporated.

The initial selection of a piece to be reproduced is made by the Director of Merchandising in cooperation with the individual manufacturers. The original antique is then withdrawn from exhibition, and copied in exact detail by the manufacturer. The original and sample copy are in time returned to Colonial Williamsburg where the sample is examined critically by the Craft Advisory Committee. If it is deficient in even the smallest detail, the sample is returned to the manufacturer for correction. When it has met the exacting standards set by Colonial Williamsburg, it is incorporated into the Reproductions Program and produced for sale.

This unusual program, beginning with the finest of antiques and continuing with their exquisite reproduction, assures each owner of an approved *Williamsburg* reproduction or adaptation of the highest quality in heirloom furniture and accessories.

CRAFT HOUSE

Craft House is the home of authentic *Williamsburg* reproductions and adaptations, made under the supervision of Williamsburg Restoration, Incorporated. In its exhibition and sales rooms, Craft House displays a wide range of furniture and accessories, as well as commemorative and souvenir items of the highest quality.

Selections from the Craft House may be ordered during a visit to the sales rooms, or by mail. Prompt attention is given to all mail orders, instructions for which may be found on page 144.

Facsimile of Certificate of Authenticity that accompanies each hallmarked reproduction

The Craft Advisory Committee, composed of members of the staff of Colonial Williamsburg, must approve all Williamsburg *Reproductions, Adaptations, and Commemorative articles before they are offered for sale.*

Williamsburg and the Hallmark

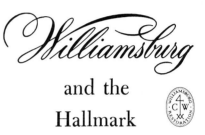

Williamsburg and the Hallmark are the registered trademarks of Williamsburg Restoration, Incorporated. Reproductions and adaptations made for Williamsburg Restoration, Incorporated, by its specially licensed manufacturers bear these registered trademarks. Products that do not bear one or both of these registered trademarks have not been approved by, nor do they have any connection with, Williamsburg Restoration, Incorporated.

The Williamsburg Hallmark is a combination of old and new symbols. The letter "C" and "W" stand for Colonial Williamsburg, the educational organization financed by the late John D. Rockefeller, Jr., and responsible for the restoration of the colonial capital of Virginia. The elongated "4" ending in a double "X" has been called the "mysterious mark" because of the many and varied stories of its origin. It appeared in seventeenth- and eighteenth-century Virginia as a shipper's or maker's mark, often combined with the initials of planters and merchants. Even earlier it had been used in England in combination with watermarks and merchants' trademarks and signs. Today this mark has been combined with Colonial Williamsburg's initials to form the Williamsburg Hallmark, a trademark that is your assurance of authenticity, quality, and value.

This bright and festive dining room was photographed in a private home in Williamsburg. The table is set with Williamsburg *airtwist stemware (page 109), silver flatware (page 106), and CW 59 pewter place plates with CW 60 pewter porringers (page 99). The handsome chandelier is the Raleigh Tavern (K12895, page 86).*

Many of the pictures in this catalogue were taken in private homes in Williamsburg. In each room the owner has combined a selection of *Williamsburg* reproductions with antique and contemporary furnishings, and with unusual paintings, fabrics, and accessories. These artistic combinations of varying styles and moods were selected to show how *Williamsburg* furniture blends with and enhances other fine furnishings, paintings, and decorative schemes. It is our hope that readers of this catalogue will enjoy these decorating ideas and will find them adaptable to their own homes.

Margaret C. McMahon
Managing Editor
Richard J. Stinely
Designer
Delmore A. Wenzel
Staff Photographer

Guide to the Catalogue

*All Prices Include Shipping Charges and Are
Subject to Change Without Notice*

DICTIONARY OF FURNITURE DESIGN

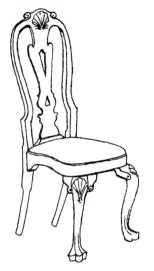

ENGLISH furniture of the eighteenth century is an unequalled expression of the cabinetmaker's art, an art that flourished to an extraordinary degree in England during the reign of Charles II and in the century that followed.

The American colonists, tied to England by blood and tradition, were naturally aware of this creative flowering and adopted the English fashion as their own. The people of eighteenth-century Williamsburg accordingly furnished their houses and public buildings in the English style, using both English imports and American pieces. Today those buildings have been restored and refurnished with English and American furniture, including examples of all the major styles from the Stuart period to the end of the eighteenth century.

English styles have become associated with the reigning monarchs of the period—William and Mary, Queen Anne, and the Georges—as well as with the designers Thomas Chippendale, the brothers Adam, George Hepplewhite, and Thomas Sheraton, whose names are synonymous with distinctive furniture designs. Although in a general way we attribute approximate dates to these various furniture periods, it is impossible to be exact. For example, the newest London fashions generally found their way to the colonies only after a considerable lapse of time. It is common, also, to use the terms "Queen Anne", "Chippendale", "Hepplewhite", and "Sheraton" when referring to American-made furniture, while it is usual in England to apply the term "Georgian"—or sometimes more specifically "George I, II, III, or IV"—to English furniture made during the period of the Georges. For the purposes of this catalogue we have chosen to use the American terms, since they are more familiar to our American audience. However, you will find the English terminology: i.e., "George I, II, or III", in brackets following the American terms, "Queen Anne", "Chippendale", "Hepplewhite", or "Sheraton". The chart below gives the relative dates when styles reached their peak of popularity and indicates the Georgian periods in England.

APPROXIMATE DATES OF PERIODS AND STYLES OF FURNITURE

Period or Style	Reigning or Working Dates	Approximate Style or Period Dates	
		ENGLAND	AMERICA
Charles II	1660-1685	1660-1690	
William & Mary	1689-1702	1690-1700	1700-1725
Queen Anne	1702-1714	1700-1715	1725-1760
Georgian			
Early: George I	1714-1727	1715-1730	
Mid: George II	1727-1760	1730-1760	
Late: George III	1760-1820	1760-1830	
George IV (Regent)	1811-1820	(includes Regency 1815-1825)	
George IV (King)	1820-1830		
Chippendale	ca. 1739-1779	1750-1765	1750-1790
Adam	ca. 1758-1792	1765-1805	
Hepplewhite	ca. 1770-1786	1780-1805	1790-1815
Sheraton	ca. 1772-1806	1790-1805	1795-1815

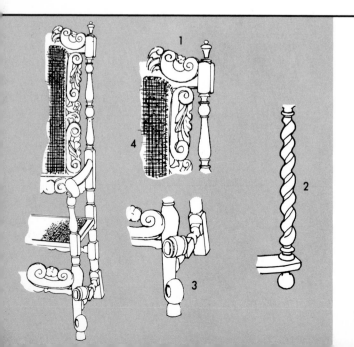

CHARLES II

WHEN Charles II was called to the throne in 1660, England joyfully shed the spartan austerity of the Cromwell period. Returning from exile on the Continent, the court brought with it an air of luxury and elaborate manners. The rectilinear lines of Cromwellian furniture were replaced with elaborate designs from the Continent. Deep carving (1) and spiral turning on legs and stretchers (2) appeared. Oak was gradually supplanted by walnut. Flemish scroll feet were used on chairs, tables, and bed terminals (3); cane chairs made their first appearance (4). Rich and bold, the style and forms developed during this period reached a peak of refinement in the following decades.

WILLIAM AND MARY

In 1688 Mary, daughter of James II, and her husband, Prince William of Orange, accepted the throne of England, bringing with them from Holland numerous craftsmen and quantities of baroque furniture. During their reign a style of furnishings emerged which was to be a transition between the elaborate forms of the Stuart period and the grace of the Queen Anne style.

Pieces distinctive of the period were china cabinets, round and oval gate-leg tables, banister-back chairs with crestings, higher bedsteads (some reached 16 feet), small tables for gaming, and the newly developed chest-on-frame (highboy) and dressing table (lowboy). Walnut was the most popular wood during this era.

Prominent characteristics of William and Mary furniture include turnings in the shape of the inverted cup (1), trumpet (2), gadrooning (3), perpendicular legs, the bun foot (4), the straight bracket foot (5), and the Spanish foot (6), with shaped stretchers often set crosswise between the legs (7).

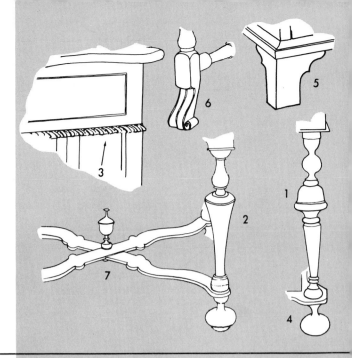

QUEEN ANNE

Queen Anne, second daughter of James II, ruled England from 1702 until 1714. The furniture style that bears her name, however, covers a period of forty years and includes the reign of George I and part of the reign of George II.

The style developed during this age of flourishing craftsmanship is considered one of the most graceful of the century. Its most distinctive feature is an undulating line based on the "S" or cyma curve—an unbroken line with a convex and concave curve. William Hogarth, the celebrated eighteenth-century English painter and engraver, called this curve the "line of beauty."

The most fashionable wood was walnut, but mahogany was introduced about 1720. With the use of this wood furniture became lighter and more graceful; and elaborate carving, to which mahogany was especially suited, began to appear.

The Queen Anne chair is perhaps the most familiar design of the period. It has an extremely comfortable splat often shaped to fit the back. Card tables with turnover hinged tops, small tables, and lower chests of drawers were popular.

Characteristics of the Queen Anne style as interpreted in America were cabriole legs (1) with numerous forms of the foot: hoof (2), pad (3), trifid (4), and slipper (5). The claw-and-ball foot was also used during this time.

Other characteristics of this style are scroll tops on chests (6), and scalloped shells on knees of legs (7) and on crests of chairs (8).

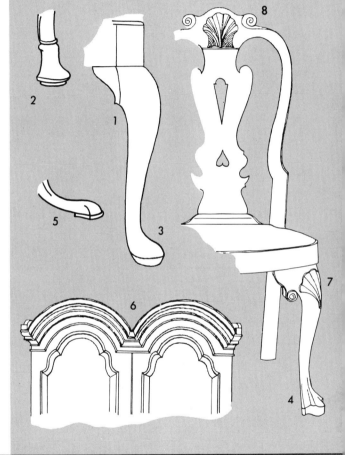

CHIPPENDALE

Thomas Chippendale, the best-known and best-advertised figure in the history of furniture-making, was born about 1705 and died in 1779. The first cabinetmaker to have his name associated with a furniture style, Chippendale was paradoxically a master of the derivative. Rarely inventive, he borrowed elements from Gothic, Chinese, and French designs and translated them into a new style.

Walnut and fruit woods, as well as mahogany, were widely used in America at this time, while English cabinetmakers preferred mahogany, an excellent wood for the crisp carving associated with Chippendale. Other popular Chippendale motifs included rococo or asymmetrical designs, simulated Chinese bamboo, the "C" scroll (1), and extensive use of fretwork.

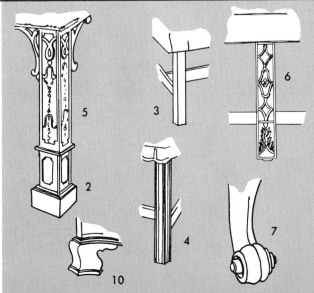

13

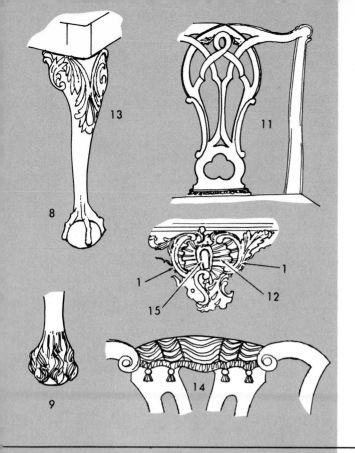

CHIPPENDALE *(Continued)*

The Chippendale straight leg, often terminating in a distinct Marlborough foot (2), was plain (3), fluted (4), carved (5), or decorated with applied frets (6). His cabriole leg was supported by the following types of feet: scroll or French toe (7), claw-and-ball (8), and hairy paw (9). The ogee bracket foot (10) was often used on case pieces. Characteristic carved forms were the pierced or interlaced splat (11), tattered shell (12), acanthus leaf (13), drapery (14), and cabochon (15).

Many of his contemporaries were his equal as designer and craftsman; but in 1754 he published *The Gentleman and Cabinet-Maker's Director*, and this established him in the public mind as one of the foremost furniture designers of the period. Two later editions of the treatise were published, the last in 1762.

These publications are known to have reached America, and the style they delineated was adapted by American cabinetmakers to suit colonial tastes. For this reason many American-made pieces have wide variations from the original designs. For example, while the highboy or chest-on-frame went out of style in most parts of England in the mid-eighteenth century, it continued in America and was developed in the American Chippendale style to include the elegant Philadelphia chest-on-chest, the Boston bombé type chest-on-chest, and the handsome Newport block front form. When we refer to "Chippendale" in this text, then, we are using the term in the American sense.

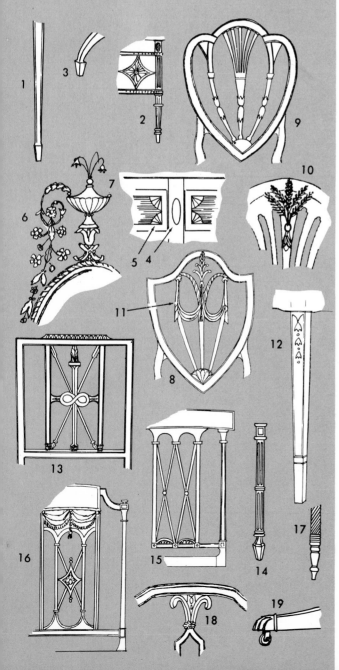

THE CLASSICAL REVIVAL

DURING the latter part of the eighteenth century Europe was swept by a wave of "classicism," inspired by renewed interest in Greek and Roman art and architecture.

In English furniture the classical revival meant the end of the elaborate, rococo Chippendale style and the introduction of the light, classical lines of Adam, Hepplewhite, and Sheraton.

Robert Adam, the best-known of three brothers, was among the first to popularize the new style in England.

Furniture in the Adam style was generally made of mahogany or satinwood, and cane-back pieces were popular. Slim tapered legs, often fluted (1, 2), were distinguishing features of the style. The legs were square or round and usually supported by block or spade (3) feet.

Classical motifs in inlay or low relief carving were widely used; ornamental discs and ovals, spandrel fans, floral swags and pendants (4, 5, 6), and most importantly the classic urn (7).

George Hepplewhite was one of the many skilled craftsmen associated with Adam in making furniture to his design. He was also important on his own as an interpreter of the classical in eighteenth-century English furniture.

Some distinguishing features of his designs include shield-shaped chair backs (8), heart-shaped backs (9), sheaves of wheat (10), carved drapery (11), bell flowers (12), prolific use of inlay, and painted designs decorating whole sets of furniture. Mahogany and satinwood were the popular woods.

American furniture of the late-eighteenth century was tremendously affected by the design books of Thomas Sheraton, and his furniture enjoyed great popularity during an affluent period in America. The celebrated Duncan Phyfe was one of many American cabinetmakers who were influenced by the Sheraton style.

Sheraton used rectangular chair backs (13), rounded and tapered legs with reeding or fluting (14), diamond and lattice designs in chair backs (15), decorative motifs of swags, flowers, and drapery (16), spiral turnings (17), Prince of Wales feathers (18), and applied brass terminals (19).

The rich colors of Schumacher's Country Linen enhance the graceful lines of Williamsburg furniture in this private home in Williamsburg. Two magnificent tables—the CW 8 Tea Table and CW 70 Tilt-Top Table—are complemented by a CW 44 Wing Chair and WA 1025 Arm Chair. Reprinted from FAMILY CIRCLE Magazine. Photographer Bill Hedrich.

Williamsburg FURNITURE
REPRODUCTIONS by Kittinger

WILLIAMSBURG Furniture Reproductions are approved copies of eighteenth-century antiques in the restored buildings of Colonial Williamsburg. These reproductions, known the world over for their distinction and unquestioned authenticity, are manufactured for Craft House by the Kittinger Company of Buffalo, New York.

Every *Williamsburg* reproduction is an exact replica of its antique prototype. Duplicates of the original fine woods are carefully selected. Solid white brass is hand-filed to the exact weight of the original mounts. Countless details of construction and decoration are meticulously hand-copied by Kittinger's master craftsmen, successors to the skilled artisans of the eighteenth century.

Discriminating householders will appreciate this fine furniture, both for its superior quality and for the timeless grace and beauty it adds to their homes.

Williamsburg furniture is made of solid mahogany unless otherwise indicated. Each piece is individually made and is available in a variety of finishes; prices quoted in this catalogue are for the standard finish. The muslin prices of upholstered pieces include the cost of applying fabric provided by the purchaser.

Please refer to the Supplemental Price List for information about antique finishes, down cushions, fabric yardage, and leather upholstery.

15

*American
Circa 1750
Queen Anne*

CW 44 WING CHAIR

The graceful proportions of this wing chair are dramatized by the turned stretchers between the cabriole legs. Made of fine mahogany, the reproduction is a faithful copy of a handsome chair in the Queen Anne style. The original, now in the Williamsburg collection, dates from about 1750. The fabric used here is Floral Bough (page 69).

Height 46″; width 36¾″; over-all depth 33½″; arm height 25½″   Muslin $540

*American
Circa 1765
Chippendale*

*American
Circa 1735-1750
Queen Anne*

CW 70 TILT-TOP TABLE

In colonial days tilt-top tables were widely used as tea tables. This authentic reproduction is a copy of a revolving tilt-top table now in the study of the George Wythe House. The Philadelphia antique, with its bird-cage construction, claw-and-ball feet, and curved legs, is a rare example of Chippendale design.

Height 28¾″; diameter 34¾″ $480

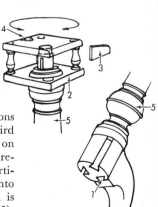

Detail of the carved claw-and-ball foot on the CW 70 Table

CW 8 TEA TABLE

The original of this elegant Queen Anne tea table now in the Peyton Randolph House was designed by a Boston cabinet-maker in the mid-eighteenth century. The reproduction copies in exact detail the graceful scallops of the apron and the delicate hand-carving of the cabriole legs. To match the original, the table is made of carefully selected mahogany with pine candle slides.

Height 26¼″; length 29¾″; depth 18½″ $385

Construction features of CW 70 Table

Legs are locked in with dovetail tenons and braced with iron support (1). Bird cage allows top to turn horizontally on pedestal (2) and is held down by a removable wedge key (3). Top tilts vertically on wooden hinge and is locked into place by a brass catch (4). Pedestal is turned from one piece of mahogany (5).

English
Circa *1760-1775*
Chippendale
(*George III*)

CW 129 SOFA

The unusual beauty of this mahogany sofa lies in the perfect proportions of its simple lines, and the grace of its long serpentine crest rail. Copied from an English antique in the Allen-Byrd House, it is unusually comfortable and seats three persons with ease. It is upholstered here in Pomegranate Resist (page 67).

Height 36″; length 79″; over-all depth 30½″; arm height 30¾″   Muslin $790

English
Circa *1730*
Queen Anne
(*George II*)

CW 2 CORNER TABLE

This Queen Anne corner table is a reproduction of an old piece now in the study of the George Wythe House. Its pad foot and graceful scalloped apron are distinctive.

Height 26¾″; diagonal width 35″; depth closed 18″, open 25″ x 25″ $350

CW 37 HANGING SHELF

This mahogany hanging shelf, a typical Thomas Chippendale design, is a reproduction of an old stand of bookshelves now used in the Governor's Palace. The four shelves and two convenient drawers are united by upright ends of delicate fretwork.

Height 39″; width 36″; depth 7″ $420

English, circa 1760
Chippendale (George III)

The CW 1½ Desk interior is fitted with nine small drawers and four pockets. Above, this practical desk is shown with the CW 152 Chair and three brass candlesticks (Pages 92-94).

*English
Circa 1760
Chippendale
(George III)*

CW 43 SMOKING CHAIR

This comfortable mahogany chair upholstered in leather is a copy of an English antique now in the little middle room of the Governor's Palace. The original, dating from about 1760, was designed for a gentleman's leisurely enjoyment of his pipe.

Height 34″; width 29″; over-all depth 24¼″; arm height 29½″   Muslin $440

Here shown in a modern setting, this classic desk is the focal point of the room. Also illustrated is its perfect complement, the CW 43 Chair. "Williamsburg in a Contemporary Setting." Designed by William E. Katzenbach, AID. Decoration and Design Show.

CW 1 SECRETARY DESK ⟶

This slant-top secretary desk with its useful bookcase is a reproduction of a fine antique in the Governor's Palace. According to the record of its purchase, the original was made in New England about 1770. The authentic reproduction shown on page 19 is an exact copy of the Chippendale piece.

Height 61″; width 41½″; depth 20½″ $1690

*American
Circa 1770
Chippendale*

Detail of the shell carving on the apron of the CW 1 Desk

CW 1½ DESK

As shown above, this desk is available without the bookcase unit on top.

Height 40″; width 41½″; depth 20½″ $1310

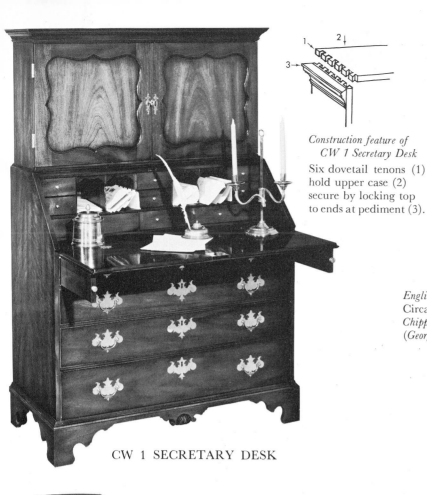

CW 1 SECRETARY DESK

*Construction feature of
CW 1 Secretary Desk*

Six dovetail tenons (1)
hold upper case (2)
secure by locking top
to ends at pediment (3).

CW 14 ARM CHAIR

Like the original which is in the Raleigh Tavern
parlor, this reproduction is made of mahogany
in the Chippendale style. The straight legs with
their delicate brackets, the graceful sweep of the
arms, and the comfortable slope of the back are
characteristics of English design of the period
after 1750. The fabric used here is Multi-Stripe
(page 68).

Height 38¾″
Width 28¼″
Over-all depth 29″
Arm height 27″
Muslin $430

*English
Circa 1760
Chippendale
(George III)*

*English
Circa 1765
Chippendale
(George III)*

CW 152 OPEN ARM CHAIR

Copied in precise detail from an antique in the
Williamsburg collection, this unusual chair has
been reproduced for use in distinctive homes and
offices. It has square legs, simple curved arms,
and rectangular front and side stretchers.

Height 38½″; width 27″; over-all depth 27″;
arm height 27½″   Muslin $395

*The excellent design of the CW 1 Desk stands out
against the varied pattern of brick and the bold Floral
Bough fabric. The CW 12 Wing Chair, CW 136
Corner Chair, and WA 1016 Bench are also featured
in this gracious room.*

As seen in HOUSE BEAUTIFUL Magazine

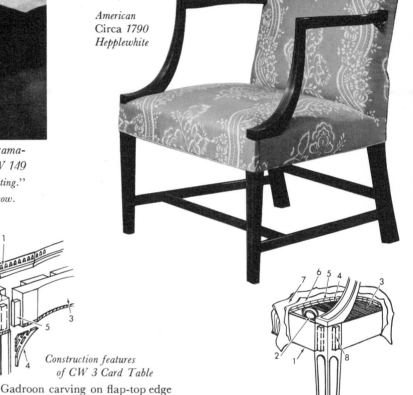

A pair of CW 13 Chairs covered in Williamsburg velvet dramatizes this contemporary setting. The CW 3 Card Table and CW 149 Kettle Stand are also shown. "Williamsburg in a Contemporary Setting." Designed by William E. Katzenbach, AID. Decoration and Design Show.

CW 13 HIS LORDSHIP'S CHAIR

This high-back Hepplewhite chair, sometimes called the Martha Washington type, is an approved reproduction of an original among the furnishings of the Raleigh Tavern. The delicate inlay, tapering legs, and slender open arms are frequently seen in the work of cabinetmakers of the late eighteenth century. The fabric shown here is Raleigh Tavern (page 67). Height 48″; width 26″; over-all depth 26½″; arm height 28″   Muslin $385

American
Circa 1790
Hepplewhite

Construction features of CW 3 Card Table

Gadroon carving on flap-top edge (1) and gavetto molding (2) lighten appearance of double top. Banded serpentine apron is from one piece of mahogany (3). Hand-carved pierced fret leg brackets (4). Mortise-and-tenon joints (5). Hand-carved rope molding (6).

Construction features of CW 13 Chair
Most *Williamsburg* upholstered pieces are constructed with webbing (1) springs (2) burlap (3) curled hair (4) cotton (5) muslin (6) and finally the cover (7). The seat rails are mortised and tenoned into the legs (8).

American
Circa 1775
Chippendale

CW 3 CARD TABLE

John Townsend, a Rhode Island cabinetmaker, is believed to have made the original of this card table, which is now in the parlor of the Brush-Everard House. Its graceful Chippendale lines are faithfully copied in the reproduction.

Height 28¾″; length 30¼″; depth 15¾″ closed, 31½″ open $395

CW 149 KETTLE STAND

This mahogany kettle stand is an exact copy of an English antique on display in the Brush-Everard House dining room. Its Georgian lines are engaging; its spun copper top is practical.

Height 21″; diameter 10″ $175

English, circa *1725-1730*
Queen Anne (George I)

American
Circa 1760
Chippendale

Detail of carved
leg and foot of
CW 19 Lowboy

CW 19 LOWBOY

This lowboy of Chippendale design is an approved reproduction of a fine antique in the Governor's Palace. The original is attributed to a Philadelphia cabinetmaker of about 1760. In the reproduction the handsome wood and delicate carving of the antique are faithfully copied.

Height 32″; length 38½″; depth 20″ $1125

American
Circa 1710-1720
William & Mary

CW 157 DRESSING TABLE

This graceful dressing table is a copy of a Pennsylvania antique now in the George Wythe House in Williamsburg. Of particular interest are the trumpet legs, characteristic of the William and Mary style, and the five convenient drawers.

Height 29½″; width 36″; depth 22¼″ $690

English
Circa 1740
Queen Anne
(George II)

CW 151
OPEN ARM CHAIR

The scroll arms and solid, shaped splat of this elegant chair are of unusual interest. Carved and finished by hand, the authentic reproduction is a faithful copy of an English antique now in the Allen-Byrd House.

Height 39¾″; width 28″; over-all depth 23½″; arm height 27¼″ Muslin $530

English
Circa 1740
Queen Anne
(George II)

CW 68 BACHELOR'S CHEST

This bachelor's chest—so-called because of its size—is a reproduction of an English piece of the mid-eighteenth century. Its fine proportions and skillfully graduated drawers mark it as the product of a master craftsman. The top slide indicates its use as a dressing stand.

Height 29¾″; width 30″; depth 17½″ $580

American
Third Quarter 18th Century
Chippendale

CW 12 WING CHAIR

A Rhode Island craftsman made the original of this chair, now in the gentlemen's reception room of the Raleigh Tavern. The handsome reproduction has the same gentle curves and sturdy construction of the antique. Of special interest is the stop fluting on the legs, a Chippendale characteristic.

Height 45½"; width 31"; over-all depth 28"; arm height 25½"   Muslin $435

CW 92 FIRE SCREEN

This approved *Williamsburg* reproduction of an English fire screen is a copy of an antique now in the George Wythe House. The stand, frame, and finial are of mahogany.

Height 47½"; panel 17¼" x 17¾"
Muslin $215

English
Circa 1760
Chippendale
(George III)

Antiques and Williamsburg *reproductions are compatible in this handsome room of a private home in Williamsburg. The CW 23 Sofa, CW 12 Wing Chair, and CW 128 Chair are shown used with a fine old desk, corner chair, and several tables. Craft House has reproductions closely resembling several of these antiques.*

Reprinted from TOWN AND COUNTRY Mag

Detail of hand-carved leg on CW 23 Sofa

English
Circa *1770*
Chippendale
(*George III*)

CW 23 SOFA

The front legs of this unusual sofa are decorated with Chinese-influenced fretwork. Smaller than the typical sofa of the period, the piece achieves distinction in the grace of its shape and the angle of its arms and back. The original is in the Governor's Palace. It is upholstered here in Spotswood (page 71).

Height 35½"; over-all length 73"; over-all depth 31½"; arm height 30"   Muslin $810

American
Circa *1750-1775*
Chippendale

English
Circa *1740*
Queen Anne
(*George II*)

CW 5 BASIN STAND

This mahogany basin stand is an approved reproduction of a fine English piece now in the Governor's Palace in Williamsburg. The CW 9 Pewter Bowl (page 100) fits into the rim of the stand, making it an unusual indoor planter. For another view of this fine reproduction, please see page 79.

Height 32"; diameter 11¾" $305

English
Circa *1740*
Queen Anne (*George II*)

CW 136 CORNER CHAIR

This corner or desk chair, often called a "roundabout chair," is distinguished by its splat back and the graceful lines of its turnings. The original was made in Pennsylvania about 1750-1775. The antique is now in the ladies' withdrawing room of the Raleigh Tavern. Height 31¼"; width 26"; over-all depth 26"; arm height 29¾"   Muslin $360

CW 147 BENCH

The original of this charming Queen Anne bench, made in England about 1740, is in the ballroom of the Governor's Palace in Williamsburg. It has been beautifully reproduced in solid mahogany.

Height 17"; length 17"; width 21½"   Muslin $210

American
Circa 1750
Chippendale

Detail of claw-
and-ball foot on
CW 134 Table

CW 134 DROP-LEAF TABLE

This handsome drop-leaf table is a copy of a New England antique now used in the library of the Brush-Everard House. The reproduction, with its pleasing oval shape and graceful legs, has retained in exact detail the clean lines and crisp hand-carving of the original.

Height 26¾″; width 13¾″ closed, 40½″ open; depth 33½″ $480

English
Circa 1740
Queen Anne
(George II)

CW 144 TABLE

The original of this graceful Queen Anne mahogany table was made about 1740. It has a concave tray top with straight skirt, slightly rounded corners, and cabriole legs terminating in pad feet. The drawer has plain bail pulls and a brass key plate.

Height 28½″; width 30¾″; depth 18¾″   Disc.

CW 156 CARD TABLE

The original of this unusual card table, made about 1725, is now used in the furnishings of Colonial Williamsburg. The claw-and-ball foot and the half-round design are rare in a piece of this early date. This authentic reproduction matches in exact detail the antique's elaborate design of scroll wings and shell with pendant leaf.

Height 28¾″; width 32¾″; depth 32¼″ open, 16⅛″ closed $695

English
Circa 1745
Chippendale
(George II)

Detail of hand-carved
leg on CW 104 Chair

CW 104 WING CHAIR

This approved *Williamsburg* reproduction, characteristically Chippendale in style, is shown here covered in Gloucester Damask (page 66). Made of mahogany, it is a copy of an English piece now used in the furnishings of Colonial Williamsburg.

Height 44″; width 33″; over-all depth 31½″; arm height 26″   Muslin $585

English
Circa 1740
Queen Anne (George II)

CW 128 SIDE CHAIR

This mahogany chair is an exact copy of an antique made about 1740 and now in the Brush-Everard House library. The cabriole legs and slightly pointed pad feet have unusual grace and dignity. This chair covered with two NP 1 needle point designs is pictured on page 82.

Height 38½″; width 23¼″; over-all depth 23″

Muslin $365

A rare antique Chinese wallpaper sets the mood of this striking room; the CW 104 Wing Chair, CW 134 Table, and CW 39 Cabinet enhance the lavish setting. On the cabinet is the Wythe House clock (page 127) and in the foreground, the CW 78 pewter inkstand (page 97). The fish bowl is the CW 41 Rummer (page 113).

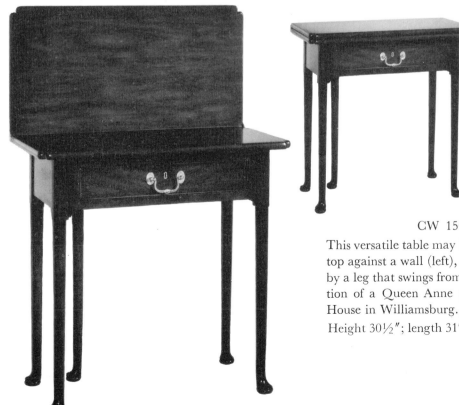

English
Mid-18th Century
Queen Anne (George III)

CW 150 CARD TABLE

This versatile table may be used closed (above), with its flap top against a wall (left), or with its top open and supported by a leg that swings from the back. It is a faithful reproduction of a Queen Anne piece now used in the Allen-Byrd House in Williamsburg.

Height 30½″; length 31″; depth 15″ closed, 30″ open $455

*American
Late 18th Century
Hepplewhite*

*American
Late 18th Century
Sheraton*

CW 27 PEMBROKE TABLE

This is a reproduction of a drop-leaf mahogany table now in the Raleigh Tavern parlor. Of American origin, it is distinguished by the holly inlay on the legs and drawers, the shape and thickness of the oval top, and the size and taper of the legs.

Height 28¼″; width 22″ closed, 46¾″ open; depth 33″ $430

CW 135 OVAL TILT-TOP TABLE

The tripod legs of this mahogany oval table terminate in spade feet in the Sheraton style of the late eighteenth century. It is an exact reproduction of the antique now on display in Craft House.

Height 27½″; length 26″; width 17¾″ $210

*English
Circa 1720
Queen Anne (George I)*

CW 141 FLAP-TOP TABLE

This unusually versatile mahogany table is equally suitable as a serving table (above left), a handsome console (above right), 'or a writing table (above center). It is an approved reproduction of an English antique now in the Williamsburg collection.

The rectangular folding top is supported on slender columnar legs terminating in turned feet. A delicate candle slide pulls out on either side; and two gates support the top when it is open. This table is pictured again on page 79.

Height 28½″; length 35¾″; depth 12″ closed, 24″ open $400

English
Circa 1760
Chippendale
(George III)

American
Third Quarter
18th Century
Hepplewhite

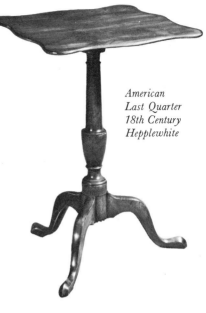

American
Last Quarter
18th Century
Hepplewhite

CW 69 SQUARE TILT-TOP TABLE

The original of this fine reproduction was made in England about 1760 and is now in the dining room of the George Wythe House. This graceful table, distinguished by its delicate tripod base and finely proportioned carved stem, is unusually sturdy, because as in all *Williamsburg* furniture each part is carefully hand-joined.

Height 26¾″; top 25⅝″ x 25⅝″ $275

CW 11 REVOLVING TILT-TOP TABLE

This authentic reproduction is a copy of a New England antique now in the parlor of the Allen-Byrd House in Williamsburg. The revolving tilt top is attached to the stem with an intricate bird-cage construction. The intermediate size of this table is distinctive.

Height 27″; diameter 21½″ $270

CW 20 TILT-TOP TABLE

The grace of this small table is enhanced by its snake feet and scalloped top. It tilts with one corner upward, becoming a delightful scalloped diamond and fitting easily into a small corner. It is a copy of a New England antique now in the Raleigh Tavern.

Height 27¼″; top 19½″ x 19½″ $170

English
Circa 1770-1790
Chippendale (George III)

CW 118 SOFA

The eighteenth-century original of this upholstered mahogany sofa is in the King's Arms Tavern in Williamsburg. The fine reproduction faithfully copies the unusual length and curved back of the English antique.

Height 35¾″; over-all length 91″; over-all depth 30″; arm height 28¾″

Muslin $825

Right. With both leaves down the CW 117 Table becomes a narrow 24 inches—perfectly suited for today's smaller apartments. Also shown: the CW 44 Wing Chair, CW 68 Chest, and CW 118 Sofa.

CW 117 GATE-LEG TABLE

An elegant and distinctive feature of this oval gate-leg table is the delicate shell and pendant design carved on the knee of each cabriole leg. The original of the table is in the supper room of the Governor's Palace in Williamsburg. The reproduction, faithfully copied in solid mahogany, provides comfortable places for as many as eight persons.

Height 29"; width 58"; length 24" closed, 70" open $800

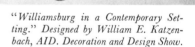

*English
Circa 1730
Queen Anne (George II)*

"Williamsburg in a Contemporary Setting." Designed by William E. Katzenbach, AID. Decoration and Design Show.

Detail of the hand-carved shell and pendant on the knee of the CW 117 Table

Construction features of CW 117 Table

A wooden hinge (1) is held in place by a special pin (2). Apron rails are locked into sides with dovetail tenons (3). Mortise-and-tenon joint (4). Apron frame is braced diagonally for extra strength (5).

The rough texture of brick and a dramatic contemporary painting are a pleasing contrast to the graceful cabriole legs and intricate carving of the CW 117 Table, and CW 146 and 142 Side Chairs. Note the unexpected use of a tall candlestand (CW 49) in the background.

American
Circa 1745
Queen Anne

As shown here, the straightforward lines of the plain table and of the simple ladder back chairs (CW 137) harmonize with those of an elaborate lowboy (CW 19). The centerpiece arrangement uses a pair of C 22 Cornucopias (page 117), and a half grapefruit fits perfectly into the CW 60 Porringer (page 99) shown here on a C 10 Delft Plate (page 118).

CW 155 SERVING TABLE

This fine marble-topped serving table is an exact copy of a Pennsylvania antique now in the Governor's Palace in Williamsburg. Made in the Queen Anne style, about 1745, this unusual table has cabriole legs on trifid feet, and is graced by delicate shell carving on the apron and front knees.
Height 27½"; length 52⅛"; depth 24" $680

English
Circa 1770
Chippendale
(George III)

← CW 16 CHAIR

This mahogany straight chair, typical of Chippendale's simpler designs, is a reproduction of an antique used in the Governor's Palace and another in the George Wythe House. Its sturdy back is graced with an unusually beautiful pierced splat. It is shown here covered in the NP 3 Needle Point (page 82).
Height 37¼"; width 22"; over-all depth 21½"
Muslin $395

English
Circa 1765
Chippendale
(George III)

CW 137 LADDER BACK CHAIR

Chairs of this style were in wide use in eighteenth-century England. This mahogany reproduction is copied from one of a complete set now in the Moody House dining room. The original was made in England during the reign of George III.
Height 36¾"; width 21"; over-all depth 21½"
Disc.

"Williamsburg Dining Room." Designed by Mary E. Dunn, FAID. Decoration and Design Show.

*A*GAINST *a rich background of silk damask draper-ies, silk-screened Palace Supper Room Wallpaper (page 73), and a rare antique needlework rug, Mary Dunn, FAID, has designed this lavish dining room using fine Williamsburg reproductions. An oval gate-leg table, the CW 117, is set with Williamsburg Potpourri dinner-ware (page 115), Airtwist goblets (page 109), and the*

famous Williamsburg sterling silver flatware (page 106). Four magnificent side chairs (CW 146) encircle the table, and a large brass chandelier (K12939, page 86) hangs above. The gilded mirror (CWLG 6, page 61) is deco-rated, like the table and chairs, with a carved shell motif. Williamsburg delft and fireplace accessories have also been used effectively.

CW 142 SIDE CHAIR

An unusual feature of this fine chair is the graceful scroll-carving flanking the knees. The original chair, one of six matching antiques used in the Governor's Palace, is upholstered in a needle point design also reproduced by Williamsburg, NP 2 (page 82).

Height 40½″; width 21¼″; over-all depth 20½″   Muslin $420

English
Circa 1740
Queen Anne (George II)

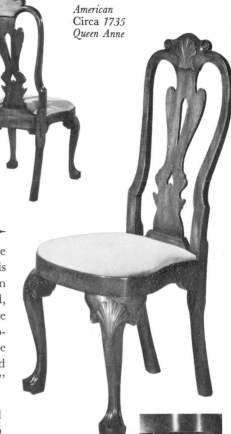

American
Circa 1735
Queen Anne

CW 146 SIDE CHAIR →

The elaborate detail of the antique has been faithfully copied in this careful reproduction of a Queen Anne mahogany chair. The original, made in Philadelphia, is in the Brush-Everard House. The reproduction has the same serpentine crest rail with centrally carved scallop shell, and "cone and heart" piercing in the splat.

Height 43¼″; width 20¼″; over-all depth 20″   Muslin $525

Detail of the hand-carved knee of the CW 142 Chair

Detail of the hand-carved leg of the CW 146 Chair

English
Circa 1725
Queen Anne
(George I)

CW 154 SETTEE

The lines of this Queen Anne settee are of an unusual elegance. The cabriole legs are defined by shaped wings and pad feet, and the outcurving arms terminate in graceful volutes. Made in England about 1725, the original is now in the Colonial Williamsburg collection. The fabric shown here is Spotswood (page 71).

Height 36¾″; length 53¾″; over-all depth 29¼″; arm height 25¾″   Muslin $750

A formal dining room in the gracious setting for the CW 33 and 34 Table in a private home in Williamsburg. Chairs used are the CW 17 and CW 17½. One leaf of the center section has been dropped to conserve space.

Reprinted from TOWN AND COUNTRY Magazine

Above, the drop-leaf center section will accommodate six persons.
$640

Below, two end sections and one center section are joined. Total length 114″. $1260

English
Late 18th Century
Hepplewhite
(George III)

Two end sections joined, form a round table 47″ in diameter. $620

CW 33 and CW 34 DINING ROOM TABLE

This solid mahogany, three-part dining room table is a faithful reproduction of a late eighteenth-century English piece now used as the dining table in the Daphne Room of the Raleigh Tavern. The simplicity of its lines are typical of the Hepplewhite style.

The drop-leaf center section alone is an excellent dining table. The two end sections locked together make a graceful round table, and they may be used separately as console tables. When these three pieces are joined a handsome long table is formed, accommodating 12 persons. The over-all length of the completed table can be adjusted by dropping one or both leaves of the center section.

The clean lines of the CW 33 Table are unusually pleasing in this contemporary dining area. The CW 17 and CW 17½ Chairs are used with it here. Eight large candles in the stunning CW 16-33 Candlesticks (page 93) light the buffet which is set with Williamsburg pottery (pages 128-129).

CW 33 and CW 34
DINING ROOM TABLE

CW 33 Center Section
Height 29¼″; width 48″;
length 22″ closed, 67″ open
$640

CW 34 End Section
Height 29¼″; width 48″;
depth 23½″ $310

*English
Circa 1770
Chippendale
(George III)*

Shown above are two end sections with one 24″ leaf, making a total length of 90½″.   48″ width $1090
57″ width $1330

Also available with additional 24″ leaf and support.   48″ width $1250
57″ width $1500

Shown above are two end sections, one center section, and two 24″ leaves, totaling 147″ in length.
48″ width $1770
57″ width $2145

An antique pedestal table now in the Allen-Byrd House was copied to make this handsome three-section dining room table. The original, made in England about 1770, has been reproduced in solid mahogany.

The center and end sections used together, or in combination with 24″ leaves, form a stunning table for a gracious dining room. As a charming small dining table, the two end sections may be fitted together, and the CW 66 alone is a handsome console table. All sections are made with tilt tops for additional use in a corner or against a wall.

This authentic reproduction is available in two widths: 57″ to match the original (CW 65-57 and CW 66-57), or 48″ (CW 65 and CW 66).

Above, two CW 66 end sections have been joined to make a charming dining table in a small contemporary room. The Queen Anne CW 128 Chairs are a graceful match for this late Chippendale table. "Williamsburg in a Contemporary Setting." Designed by William E. Katzenbach, AID. Decoration and Design Show.

Here shown in a traditional Williamsburg home, this dining table is used in its extended length with the CW 142 Side Chairs. The interesting gold wallpaper is Mandarin and Pine Tree (page 78).

This large room in an up-to-date house uses Williamsburg *reproductions throughout the combination living/dining area. For the dining room a CW 33 and four CW 17 Chairs have been chosen; the CW 43 Smoking Chair, CW 12 Wing Chair, and the sleek CW 148 Sideboard are prominently displayed in the living room.*

Reprinted from *TOWN AND COUNTRY* Magazine

*American
Late 18th Century
Chippendale*

CW 17 CHAIR

The original of this fine Chippendale chair, made in Philadelphia in the late eighteenth century, is on display at Craft House in Williamsburg. The reproduction is shown here covered in Spotswood (page 71).

Height 37½″; width 22½″; over-all depth 23¾″.
Muslin $340

CW 17½ ARM CHAIR

This comfortable arm chair may be used alone at a desk or with several CW 17 Chairs around a dining table. It is made of solid mahogany.

Height 37½″; width 25″; over-all depth 24½″; arm height 26¾″   Muslin $420

CW 47 ARM CHAIR and CW 47½ SIDE CHAIR

These chairs are meticulous copies of English antiques now in the Daphne Room of the Raleigh Tavern. Carefully reproduced in mahogany, they add distinction to any room, whether used alone at a desk or together at a dining room table. They are shown here covered in Multi-Stripe (page 68).

CW 47 ARM CHAIR

Height 37¾″; width 26″; over-all depth 22½″; arm height 27″   Muslin $390

CW 47½ SIDE CHAIR

Height 37¾″; width 22¼″; over-all depth 22″

Muslin $300

Detail of carving on arm post of CW 47 Chair

English
Circa 1765
Chippendale (George III)

English
Circa 1740
Queen Anne
(George II)

CW 148 SIDEBOARD

Copied from an English antique of about 1740, this low sideboard has unusual brasses, paneled sides, and cross-banded mahogany encircling the drawers. The original is now in the Raleigh Tavern in Williamsburg. It is illustrated again on page 59.
Height 33¾″; length 77½″; depth 21¼″ $945

Construction features of CW 148 Sideboard
Custom-made oval brass knobs with nickel silver insert through center (1). Cross-banded border of mahogany (2). Dovetail tenons (3).

CW 153 HIGHBOY

This handsome Chippendale highboy, distinguished by its vigorously scalloped skirt, has been reproduced from an American antique now in the upstairs hall of the George Wythe House. The original is believed to have been made in New Jersey about 1760.

Height 69¾"; width 42¾"; depth 22⅞" $1485

American
Circa 1760
Chippendale

English
Mid-18th Century
Chippendale
(George III)

CW 57 TABLE

This mahogany bedside table is an approved reproduction of an English antique in the Governor's Palace. The scalloped gallery with pierced hand-holes is a distinctive feature of this Chippendale piece, as are the delicate leg brackets and the paneled doors.

Height 31"; width 21"; depth 19¼"
$445

CW 87 SIDEBOARD

Copied from an antique now in use at Christiana Campbell's Tavern, this small sideboard has four tapered square legs in front, two in the rear. Octagonal key escutcheons and heavy round brasses are distinctive features of this simple design.

Height 40½"; length 57"; depth 20¼"
$680

American
Late 18th Century
Sheraton

American
Circa 1770
Chippendale

CW 143 CHEST

The simple lines of this Chippendale piece are enhanced by the bracket feet and fluted, chamfered front corners. It is an exact reproduction of a fine antique now in the Market Square Tavern in Williamsburg.

Height 40¼"; width 38½"; over-all depth 20¼"

$855

CW 49 CANDLESTAND

An English provincial piece in the Governor's Palace was copied to make this mahogany candlestand. The authentic reproduction matches in every detail the antique's galleried octagonal top, simple turnings, and spreading tripod base with pad feet.

Height 38½"; top 10½" x 10½"

English
Circa 1740
Queen Anne
(George II)

$175

CW 145 DRESSING TABLE

The original of this mahogany dressing table is a Philadelphia piece of the mid-eighteenth century now in the Williamsburg collection. The elegance of the antique is faithfully reproduced in the shell and leaf carving on the knees, the shaped and molded cabriole legs, and the carved web feet with fluted stockings.

Height 28¼"; length 35"; depth 19½"

$670

American
Mid-18th Century
Queen Anne

Detail of carving on knee of CW 145 Table

Detail of fluted stocking and web foot of the CW 145 Table

American
Circa 1760
Chippendale

CW 18 CHEST

This chest is a meticulous reproduction of an antique mahogany chest of drawers now used in the George Wythe House. Of Chippendale design, it is distinguished by its graduated drawers, bracket feet, reeded quarter-round columns, and graceful brass drawer pulls.

Height 35½"; width 38¼"; depth 19½" $775

Construction features of CW 18 Chest

Drawer runners (or dust panels) are tenoned into ends (1). Drawers are dovetailed front (2) and back (not shown). Cock bead is around each drawer (3). Custom hardware is used (4). Fluted quarter-round column pilasters cover complex joinery of chest frame (5).

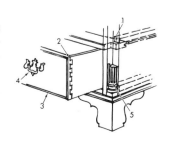

American
Circa *1760-1775*
Chippendale

Detail of claw-and-ball
foot on CW 139 Bed

*A pair of CW 139½ twin beds is enhanced by the bold stripe
fabric used as bed hangings and covers. Notice the curved design in
the canopy, a striking contrast to the stark stripes.*

CW 139 DOUBLE BED

The original of this tall-post Chippendale bedstead was
made in New England in the second half of the eighteenth
century and is now in the Brush-Everard House in Williamsburg. Faithfully reproduced in solid mahogany, it has a flat
canopy and square, tapered headposts united by an arched
headboard. Its fluted footposts are on cabriole legs which
end in vigorously carved claw-and-ball feet. The CW 139
Double Bed can be seen on page 63.

Height 87¾″; width 61½″; length 82¼″ $890

CW 139½ SINGLE BED

The handsome bedstead described above is also available
as a single bed.

Height 87¾″; width 46½″; length 82¼″ $870

Both beds use standard springs and mattresses.

Bed frame showing construction

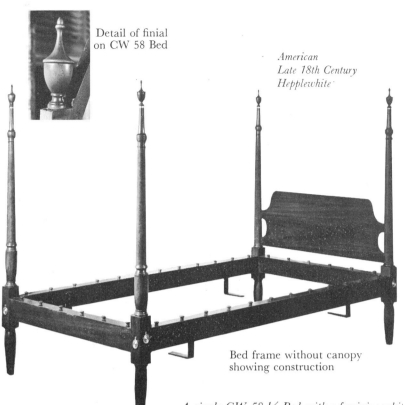

Detail of finial
on CW 58 Bed

*American
Late 18th Century
Hepplewhite*

Bed frame without canopy
showing construction

CW 58 DOUBLE BED

This bed, with mahogany frame and maple side rails, is a reproduction of a New England antique of the late eighteenth century. It is an excellent example of the simpler designs often used in that period, in contrast to the frequently elaborate and intricately carved pieces of the early and middle years of the century. In this careful reproduction the posts are small and the canopy frame light and gracefully arched. This type of bed was often used without a canopy and is available either way.

Height 58½″ (with canopy 77⅛″); width 59⅜″;
length 81⅜″ $575

Canopy $95

CW 58½ SINGLE BED

The fine bed described above is also available as a single bed.

Height 58½″ (with canopy 77⅛″); width 44⅜″;
length 81⅜″ $550

Canopy $95

Both beds use standard springs and mattresses.

A single CW 58 ½ Bed with a feminine white ruffled canopy is a charming focal point in this small bedroom. The fabric of the quilted bedcover is Plantation Calico (page 68) and the wing chair (CW 12) is upholstered in Country Linen (page 67). The CW 58 Double Bed is illustrated on page 62.

Williamsburg

FURNITURE ADAPTATIONS

by Kittinger

WILLIAMSBURG Furniture Adaptations, produced for Craft House by the Kittinger Company, were inspired by the handsome antiques in the restored buildings of Colonial Williamsburg. Whereas reproductions are always exact replicas of antiques, adaptations are made by modern construction methods when desirable and in some cases are redesigned for modern comfort. Thus simplified in line and style, *Williamsburg* adaptations combine the traditional charm of eighteenth-century design with the ease of twentieth-century living.

The alterations in construction and design of *Williamsburg* adaptations are supervised by the Craft Advisory Committee, a select group of Colonial Williamsburg experts. The Committee is careful to retain the essential spirit of the antique while incorporating the most desirable modern variations. Their recommendations include only the most thoughtful, discriminating alterations and are guided always by a meticulous adherence to the principles of good design.

For example, the WA 1005 Sofa has been lowered by one inch, shortened by four inches, and is two and a half inches shallower. In addition, it has six legs instead of the eight of the original, the back stretcher has been eliminated, and modern upholstery is used for added comfort.

Storage problems have been solved with compartmented drawers and cabinets and deeper shelves. The smaller homes of today have been acknowledged through a general scaling-down of proportions. Comfort has been heightened by softer upholstery, springs, more leg room under dining room tables, and higher chairs.

Modifications vary, of course, from adaptation to adaptation. The WA 1020 Table is exactly like the original with the exception of its internal construction which makes use of the best up-to-date methods. On the other hand, the handsome WA 1027 China Cupboard has been lowered in height nine inches, narrowed six inches, and the depth of its bottom section reduced one and a half inches. In addition, the cupboard has been fully fitted with compartmented interiors for proper silver and china storage.

Carefully and thoughtfully, then, *Williamsburg* adaptations are modified in varied ways to combine the best of the traditional style with the best of contemporary design. The result is a line of unusual furniture, graced with the fine proportions and details of the best antiques, and eminently suited to the graciousness of today's most distinguished homes.

Williamsburg adaptations are made of the finest mahogany unless otherwise indicated. Each piece of furniture is individually made and is available in a number of finishes; prices quoted in this catalogue are for the standard finish. In the case of the upholstered pieces, prices are quoted in muslin and include the cost of applying fabric provided by the purchaser. Further information about *Williamsburg* adaptations is given in the Supplemental Price List.

LEFT

The living room in a colonial home in Williamsburg showing the WA 1005 Sofa (upholstered in Jones Toile), WA 1011 Chair, WA 1035 Coffee Table, and WA 1012 Wing Chair.

RIGHT

The traditional lines of Williamsburg *Adaptation Furniture are ideally suited to this modern living area. Shown here are the WA 1035 Coffee Table, two matching WA 1016 Benches, the WA 1012 Wing Chair, WA 1045 Card Table, and WA 1025 Arm Chair. On the window sill are three handsome C 45 delft vases (page 120).*

American
Circa *1770*
Chippendale

WA 1005 SOFA

The lean grace of the original Chippendale sofa has been matched in this elegant adaptation. The back has the unusual humpbacked silhouette which is characteristic of the old piece now on display in the Raleigh Tavern parlor. The fabric shown here is Bellflower (page 70).

Height 36¼″; over-all length 84″; over-all depth 32½″; arm height 30½″

Muslin $580

WA 1033 COFFEE TABLE

This striking coffee table was adapted from the bench section of a day bed now on display in the library of the Brush-Everard House. It is distinguished by finely turned stretchers and graceful Queen Anne legs. The antique day bed was made in Rhode Island.

Height 17¾″; length 46″; width 22½″

$290

This dramatic room is proof that traditional and modern design can be exciting partners. The WA 1005 Sofa upholstered in Spotswood is a graceful foil for the soaring window and slate floor. With the sofa are a CW 128 Chair and a WA 1033 Table.

American
Circa *1730-1740*
Queen Anne

WA 1031 BACHELOR'S CHEST

This adaptation of an English Chippendale chest now in the Raleigh Tavern faithfully reflects the dramatic lines of the original. It is made of beautifully grained mahogany, and embellished with fine brasses on the sides and front.

Height 30½″; length 31¼″; depth 18″ $410

English
Circa 1750
Chippendale (George II)

In this delightful room the WA 1031 Bachelor's Chest is used as a small desk with the WA 1016 Bench. WA 1011 Chairs are placed on either side of the hearth.

English
Late 18th Century
Chippendale (George III)

WA 1042 COFFEE TABLE

An antique tray was faithfully copied to make the top of this charming coffee table. The base of the table was especially designed to match the graceful shape of the tray.

Height 21½″; width 27¾″; depth 21¾″ $185

43

English
Circa *1770*
Chippendale
(*George III*)

WA 1037 DESK

This fine Chippendale desk was copied from an English antique made about 1770. The frame on which it rests was carefully designed to match the lines and spirit of the antique. In this charming adaptation the leather writing surface has been replaced by mahogany. The lid and two lower drawers have fine brass locks.

Height 38″; width 26½″; depth 21″; height of writing bed 29″ $460

The WA 1037 Desk is here shown with the WA 1038-24 Hanging Shelf and a CW 142 Side Chair. On the shelf are a group of pewter reproductions and a row of Doulton Character Jugs from Williamsburg (page 124).

English
Circa *1760*
Chippendale (George III)

WA 1038 SHELF

Antique shelves now hanging in the George Wythe House inspired this careful adaptation. Trellis sides terminating in scroll crestings unite four shelves and a graceful drawer.

Height 34″; width 30″; depth 7″ $230

WA 1038-24 SHELF

Same as above, 24″ width $230

WA 1037 Desk with slant top closed showing the handsome Chippendale brasses with locks on the two lower drawers and lid.

WA 1012 WING CHAIR

Modeled after a rare wing chair in the Brush-Everard House, this adaptation has the same magnificent bow in the upper wing; a thicker cushion has been added for extra comfort. The fabric shown here is Plantation Calico (page 68).

Height 45″; width 32″; over-all depth 32″; arm height 24″　　　　　　　　　　　Muslin $365

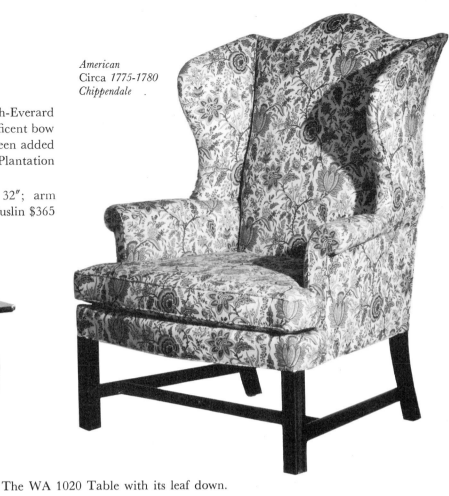

American
Circa 1775-1780
Chippendale

The WA 1020 Table with its leaf down.

A rich contemporary painting by Justin Curry is the background for the WA 1012 Chair, 1020 Table, and 1016 Bench, graceful furnishings in a traditional style.

American
Circa 1730-1740
Queen Anne

WA 1020 DROP-LEAF TABLE

The graceful lines, cabriole legs, and pad feet of a fine antique in the Brush-Everard House have been carefully reproduced in this elegant Queen Anne single-drop-leaf table. The only changes in the adaptation are in unseen interior construction details. A Massachusetts craftsman made the original about 1730-1740.

Height 25¾″; length 31″; width 23½″ open, 13½″ closed　　　　　　　　　　　　　　$250

American
Circa 1770
Chippendale

WA 1025 OPEN ARM CHAIR

An American antique now in the Wythe House study was the inspiration for this fine Chippendale chair, shown here covered in leather, studded with handsome brass nailheads. Its deep seat and boldly raked back make it unusually comfortable. It is also effective upholstered in fabric, without nailheads.

Height 43½″; width 27¾″; over-all depth 27¼″; arm height 27¼″   Muslin $275

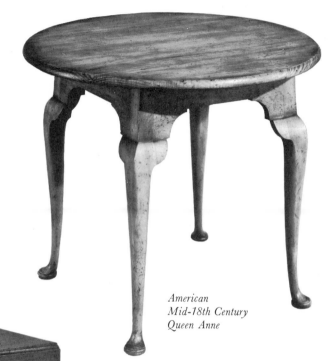

American
Mid-18th Century
Queen Anne

WA 1045 CARD TABLE

The pleasing lines of an American antique have been faithfully copied in this striking card table. Of unusual interest are the flared cabriole legs, and the skirt which has been nicely arched to provide ample knee room. Like the antique, the top and apron are pine and the legs are maple.

Height 27¼″; diameter 33″ $240

American
Last Half 18th Century
Queen Anne

American
Circa 1770
Chippendale

WA 1010 TABLE

Delicately balanced on a graceful tripod, this mahogany Queen Anne table is an adaptation of an American antique now in the Wythe House parlor. Today, as in the eighteenth century, round tables of this type were popular as small occasional or end tables.

Height 26¾″; top diameter 20¼″ $150

WA 1035 DROP-LEAF COFFEE TABLE

This twentieth-century coffee table—a form unknown in the eighteenth century—has been adapted from a small mahogany drop-leaf table in the Williamsburg collection. The dimensions of the antique have been reduced in proper proportions to form this table of delightful simplicity.

Height 18¾″; width 35″ open, 20⅛″ closed; length 42″ $255

English
Circa *1760*
Chippendale (*George III*)

English
Circa *1760-1775*
Chippendale (*George III*)

WA 1014 TABLE

The straightforward simplicity of the antique is matched in this fine Chippendale table. Unlike the original, the adaptation is finished on the back so that it may be used as a free-standing table. The mahogany original is in the Wigmaker's Shop in Williamsburg.

Height 28″; width 28¾″; depth 16″ $150

WA 1009 TABLE

The antique after which this tripod table was patterned is a George III piece, *circa* 1760-1775, now used in the Brush-Everard House. The original has been simplified in this graceful mahogany adaptation to create a sturdy occasional table.

Height 27¼″; top 25″ x 25″ $150

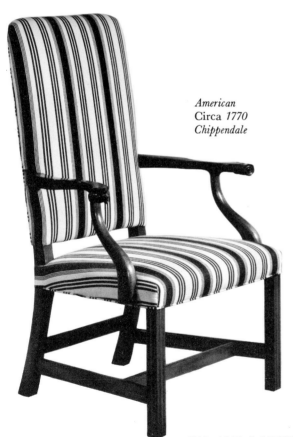

American
Circa *1770*
Chippendale

A WA 1040 Chair, upholstered in woven Apples (page 69), and a WA 1014 Table make a pleasant pair in this feminine bedroom. The print behind the chair is one of Furber's Floral Prints (page 84).

WA 1040 LADY'S CHAIR

This handsome Chippendale chair, shown here covered in Multi-Stripe, was adapted from an antique now in the George Wythe House. In the adaptation the back has been given more pitch and the seat more depth for added comfort.

Height 41″; width 27½″; over-all depth 21½″; arm height 24¾″   Muslin $295

English
Last Half 18th Century
Hepplewhite (George III)

WA 1047 WING CHAIR

An English antique in the Raleigh Tavern inspired this graceful *Williamsburg* adaptation. The saddle seat wings of the original are carefully copied here, as are the unusually fine proportions of the rolled arms. In the adaptation, shown here covered in Wythe House Border Resist (page 65), the taper of the front legs has been increased, and the chair has been lowered slightly.

Height 45″; over-all width 29″; over-all depth 28″; arm height 27½″   Muslin $375

Accents of orange enrich this striking room which features Williamsburg *Furniture Adaptations. A WA 1047 Chair, upholstered in Wythe House Border Resist (page 65), a WA 1011 Chair covered in Country Linen (page 67), and a Pembroke table, WA 1006, are the center of interest. Four handsome Williamsburg brass candlesticks are grouped on the mantle.*

American
Mid-18th Century
Chippendale

WA 1008 CHEST OF DRAWERS

The gracious size and design of this Chippendale chest were borrowed from a Virginia antique now in the Market Square Tavern in Williamsburg. Like the original, the adaptation has four deep drawers and two small ones.
Height 46¼″; width 40″; depth 20″ $495

American
Circa 1765-1770
Chippendale

WA 1011 OPEN ARM CHAIR

This small open arm chair was inspired by an American antique now in the George Wythe House. The graceful Chippendale lines of the original are faithfully reflected and its comfort enhanced by extra height and additional pitch in the back. It is shown here covered in Raleigh Tavern linen (page 67).
Height 39″; width 24″; over-all depth 27¼″; arm height 25¾″   Muslin $235

American
Late 18th Century
Hepplewhite

WA 1006 PEMBROKE TABLE

Hepplewhite Pembroke is redefined in this *Williamsburg* adaptation. The classic design has been given a fresh look by the use of molding instead of inlay around the drawer and leaves. The original table is now used in the furnishings of Colonial Williamsburg.
Height 28″; width 39″ open, 20¾″ closed; depth 29¾″ $250

English
Circa *1750*
Chippendale (George II)

WA 1030 COMMODE

An English antique commode now in the Brush-Everard House was the inspiration for this handsome side table. The two shelves hold books, magazines, and accessories; the deep drawer is a practical addition.

Height 31½″; width 23¼″; depth 19″ $245

In this feminine bedroom a WA 1004 is used as a dressing table with the WA 1016 Bench and WA 1028 Mirror (page 61). Williamsburg figurines and wooden accessories are charming accents on the table.

English
Circa *1760*
Chippendale (George III)

WA 1016 BENCH

Except for changes in construction methods, this sturdy bench is an exact copy of an English antique in the Williamsburg collection. The original was made about 1760.

Height 16¾″; width 19¾″; depth 15¾″
Muslin $105

American
Circa *1750-1775*
Chippendale

WA 1004 TABLE

This fine Chippendale adaptation may be used as a dressing table, small desk, or serving table. The Virginia antique from which it was modeled is in the Raleigh Tavern parlor.

Height 29½″; width 42″; depth 21″ $250

WA 1046 SIDE CHAIR

The original of this fine chair, designed by a New England craftsman about 1760, is in the Brush-Everard House in Williamsburg. Its excellent proportions and pleasing serpentine crest rail have been carefully incorporated into the adaptation, shown here covered in Bombay (page 65).

Height 37¾"; width 22¾"; overall depth 23½"   Muslin $230

American
Circa 1760
Chippendale

A man would be pleased with this WA 1002 Chest and complementary Chippendale mirror (WA 1032, page 61). A handsome wooden box (page 126) is used as a practical catch-all. A group of brass candlesticks makes a handsome composition on the chest.

American
Late 18th Century
Hepplewhite

WA 1029 TABLE

This graceful Hepplewhite table was inspired by an American antique now among the furnishings of a Williamsburg Inn guest cottage. The slightly tapered legs and appealing proportions are exactly like those of the original.

Height 29½"; width 25¼"; depth 18¾" $135

American
Circa 1775
Chippendale

WA 1002 CHEST OF DRAWERS

An antique made in Virginia about 1775 was adapted to make this medium-sized Chippendale chest of drawers. Free of embellishments such as locks and escutcheons, the adaptation has the clean lines and simple elegance of the fine antique.

Height 35¼"; width 37½"; depth 21¾" $385

THE Morgan-Jones Queen Anne Bedspread (page 63) is a rich covering for the WA 1003 Half Canopy Bed shown here in a gracious traditional bedroom. The canopy may also be hung with straight draperies and a tailored valance.

HALF CANOPY BED

A New England folding or press bed now in the Raleigh Tavern was the inspiration for this adaptation bed shown here covered with the Queen Anne bedspread. The adaptation has borrowed the antique's essential grace and purity of line, though the folding feature has been eliminated.

WA 1003 Double Canopy Bed
Height 79½″; width 56½″; length 79½″ $290

WA 1003½ Single Canopy Bed
Height 79½″; width 41½″; length 79½″ $270

Both beds use standard springs and mattresses. Standard side rails for the WA 1003 and the WA 1003½ Beds are 75″. They are available, however, in 78″ and 81″ lengths at no additional cost.

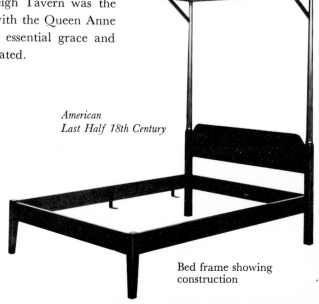

*American
Last Half 18th Century*

Bed frame showing
construction

LOW-POST BED

The precedent for this design is an antique made in Newport, Rhode Island, and used now in the Brush-Everard House. This fine adaptation copies the curved headboard of the original, and has the same deep fluting on the low posts. It is shown here with the Raleigh Tavern bedspread (page 63).

American
Circa 1760-1770
Chippendale

WA 1034 Double Bed
Height 40¼″; length 79½″; width 56½″ $245

WA 1034½ Single Bed
Height 40¼″; length 79½″; width 41½″ $225

Both beds use standard springs and mattresses. Standard side rails for the WA 1034 and WA 1034½ Beds are 75″. They are available, however, in 78″ and 81″ lengths at no additional cost.

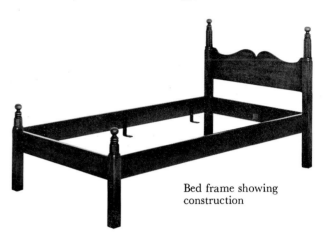

Bed frame showing construction

A single WA 1034½ Bed is the focal point in this contemporary room. The Raleigh Tavern bedspread (page 63) reflects the paneled design of the wooden wall. The CW 57 Cabinet, the WA 1035 Coffee Table unexpectedly placed beside the bed, and a CW 128 Chair in glowing orange velvet all contribute to the drama of this gracious room.

WA 1017-1 SIDEBOARD

A Hepplewhite low cupboard now in the Williamsburg collection inspired this unusual sideboard made of fine mahogany and fitted with brass escutcheons and hinges. The original was probably used both as a sideboard and for clothes storage. For the modern owner, it has been scaled down and fitted inside with two silver-storage drawers and six adjustable shelves. Also, the middle compartment now opens for additional storage space.

Height 36″; length 66″; depth 20¾″ $695

American
Last Half 18th Century
Transitional: Chippendale-Hepplewhite

WA 1018 SIDE CHAIR and WA 1118 ARM CHAIR

A Chippendale side chair made in Virginia about 1760-1780 inspired this charming chair design. The adaptation has borrowed the antique's sturdy back and simple pierced splat. The arms were designed from another Chippendale model of the same period. These chairs are also available with upholstered seats (WA 1048 and WA 1148).

American
Circa 1770
Chippendale

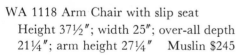

WA 1118

WA 1148

WA 1018

WA 1048

WA 1118 Arm Chair with slip seat
  Height 37½″; width 25″; over-all depth
  21¼″; arm height 27¼″   Muslin $245

WA 1148 Arm Chair with upholstered seat
  Height 37½″; width 25″; over-all depth
  21¼″; arm height 27¼″   Muslin $245

WA 1018 Side Chair with slip seat
  Height 37½″; width 21″; over-all depth
  20″   Muslin $175

WA 1048 Side Chair with upholstered seat
  Height 37½″; width 21″; over-all depth
  20″   Muslin $175

WA 1024 SERVING TABLE

The unusual reduced scale of this sideboard makes it particularly suitable for a small dining room or as a second serving table in a larger room. A sliding, removable tray for silver fits into one of the drawers. It was adapted from a Hepplewhite antique used in the King's Arms Tavern.

Height 34¼″; length 47¾″; depth 20½″ $285

American
Late 18th Century
Hepplewhite

Rough-hewn beams and pine-paneled walls enhance the delicate charm of a WA 1022 Table and WA 1024 Sideboard in this exciting room. CW 137 Chairs are used around the table, and a length of Jones Toile has been converted into a stunning Roman shade.

WA 1022 DROP-LEAF TABLE

A handsome small dining table, this Queen Anne adaptation was inspired by an antique made in Virginia and now in Christiana Campbell's Tavern in Williamsburg. It is distinguished by its short leaves and graceful legs on pad feet.

Height 29½″; length 42¾″; width 43″ open, 16½″ closed $325

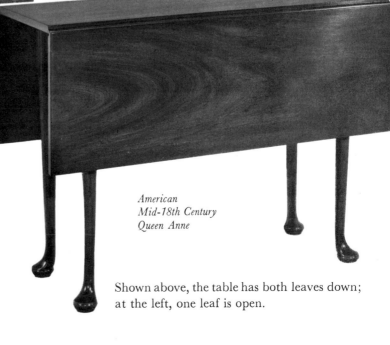

American
Mid-18th Century
Queen Anne

Shown above, the table has both leaves down; at the left, one leaf is open.

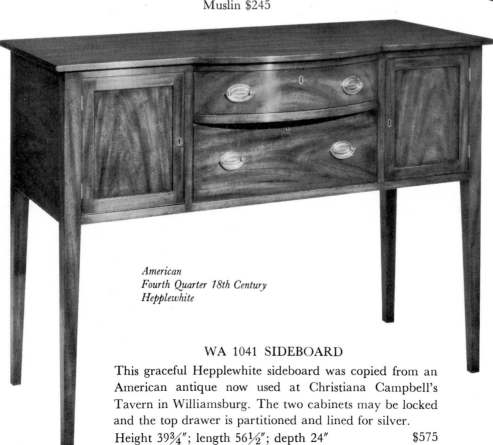

WA 1019 SIDE CHAIR and WA 1119 ARM CHAIR

The gentle curve at the top of these chairs and in the arms is characteristic of the simpler Queen Anne style. For added comfort the adaptations have upholstered rather than slip seats. Both the antique side chair and the arm chair from which this pair was redesigned are in the Raleigh Tavern. The chairs are shown here covered in woven Apples (page 69).

English
Second Quarter 18th Century
Queen Anne (George II)

WA 1019 Side Chair
Height 38″; width 21¼″; over-all
depth 21½″   Muslin $175

WA 1119 Arm Chair
Height 38″; width 26″; over-all
depth 23½″; arm height 28¼″
                    Muslin $245

American
Fourth Quarter 18th Century
Hepplewhite

WA 1041 SIDEBOARD

This graceful Hepplewhite sideboard was copied from an American antique now used at Christiana Campbell's Tavern in Williamsburg. The two cabinets may be locked and the top drawer is partitioned and lined for silver.
Height 39¾″; length 56½″; depth 24″ $575

The practical and versatile WA Pedestal Table is here used with two ends joined to become a compact dining table in a small room. In the background is a WA 1041 Sideboard, and WA 1019 Chairs are used around the table. As a centerpiece four C 30 delft jars (page 120) have been filled with grapes.

PEDESTAL DINING ROOM TABLE

This three-part dining room table was inspired by an American antique now used in the furnishings of Colonial Williamsburg. Together, the three sections form a graceful table 108 inches in length. Similarly, the end sections joined to each other make a distinctive table for a small room; they may also be used separately as consoles or serving tables. Eighteen-inch leaves are available to increase the length of this versatile pedestal table.

The dimensions of the antique have been reduced in the adaptation, and the angle of the legs has been changed for comfort and added stability. In addition, the drop leaves of the original end sections have been modified into the more popular console style.

WA 1043 Center Section
Height 29½″; width 46″; length 36″ $395

WA 1044 End Section
Height 29½″; width 46″; length 36″ $375

*American
Late 18th Century
Sheraton*

Two end sections joined together for a total length of 72″ $750
Above table with one 18″ leaf $830

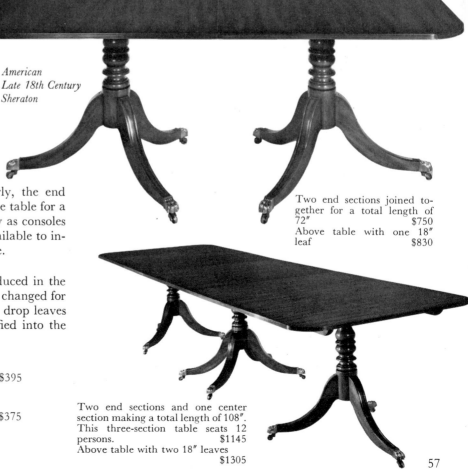

Two end sections and one center section making a total length of 108″. This three-section table seats 12 persons. $1145
Above table with two 18″ leaves $1305

English
Circa *1770*
Hepplewhite
(*George III*)

WA 1026
DROP-LEAF TABLE

A table once owned by Lucy Ludwell Paradise, an eighteenth-century Williamsburg resident, inspired this magnificent Hepplewhite drop-leaf table. The dimensions of the original have been slightly adjusted in this adaptation, and two legs have been added for increased strength and stability.

Height 29½"; width 48"; length 76" open, 28" closed
$425

WA 1026 Drop-Leaf Table and two WA 1049 Console Ends, a total length of 124" $855

WA 1049 CONSOLE END

A console end, shown above, which attaches to the large table or which can be used by itself as a handsome wall table, is also available.

Height 29½"; width 48"; depth 24" $215

American
Circa *1760*

WA 1027-1 CHEST

This handsome adaptation chest, described below, may be used alone or as the lower section of the WA 1027 China Cabinet.

Height 38"; width 48¾"; depth 18½"   Disc.

WA 1027 CHINA CABINET

The dimensions of an antique Pennsylvania dresser in the Williamsburg collection have been considerably reduced to make this adaptation china cabinet (shown left). Each section has two adjustable shelves, those in the upper section being grooved to hold plates. The lower section, which may be used alone as a chest, also has two drawers (with a four-drawer effect), one of them lined and partitioned for silver.

Height 81"; width 51⅜"; depth 18½"   Disc.

In this gracious hallway the CWLG 7 Mirror is appropriately placed over a Queen Anne sideboard (CW 148, page 35). The antique rose medallion vase and dish subtly complement the Chinese motif of the frame.

Williamsburg MIRRORS

By
Friedman Brothers Decorative Arts

FROM the Middle Ages to our own time, mirrors have been used to decorate the handsomest rooms. Called "looking glasses" until the late nineteenth century, mirrors were once a symbol of wealth and luxury and were used lavishly by the rich, sometimes even to line an entire wall or room.

Today's distinctive homes also make use of the decorative value of mirrors. Combined with a group of pictures, or used alone over a console or chest of drawers, they add life and dimension to every room where they hang.

Included in this selection of *Williamsburg* Mirror Reproductions by Friedman Brothers of New York are examples of the more elaborate as well as the simpler styles of the colonial period. The originals hang in the restored buildings of Colonial Williamsburg. The copies have been faithfully reproduced by master craftsmen.

CWLG 4

Gilded designs of birds and plant life decorate the lacquered frame of this elegant mirror. The original, now in the Norton-Cole House, was made about 1715 in England. Of interest is the two-plate mirror, typical of long Queen Anne looking glasses. It is available with a red or black lacquer frame. Glass 14½" x 39½"; over-all size 18" x 43"

Red or black $250

CWLG 7

The black lacquer frame of this handsome Queen Anne mirror is enriched with lush decorations of Chinese birds and plants. The original, made in England about 1715, may be seen today in the West Flanking Building of the Governor's Palace. This mirror is also available with a red lacquer frame. Glass 15" x 44¼"; over-all size 18¾" x 48"

Red or black $310

CWLG 7   CWLG 4

CWLG 10 and CWLG 11

These handsome looking glasses are exact copies of English antiques now in the Williamsburg collection. The originals, Queen Anne in style, were made about 1725. In these fine reproductions the glass is beveled to follow the graceful outlines of the frame. Both are available as wall mirrors, or with an easel back for use on a dressing table or chest of drawers.

CWLG 10. Frame available in either polished or antique gold. Glass 15″ x 21¼″; over-all size 15¾″ x 22″

Easel mirror	$170
Wall mirror	150

CWLG 11. Frame available in antique gold, polished gold, or black. Glass 13¼″ x 23¼″; over-all size 14¾″ x 24¾″

Black easel mirror	$160
Black wall mirror	140
Gold easel mirror	170
Gold wall mirror	150

CWLG 3

This elegant Adam-style mirror is a copy of a late-eighteenth-century antique hanging now in the Daphne Room of the Raleigh Tavern. The oval glass is framed in gold leaf with an elaborate design of urn, flowers, and leaves. Glass 15½″ x 25½″; over-all size 22″ x 49½″
$360

The CWLG 11 with easel is here used on the CW 145 Dressing Table (page 37).

CWLG 5

Richly adorned with gold leaf Prince of Wales feathers, this Georgian mirror is framed in delicately carved burl walnut. The original English looking glass, now a part of the furnishings of the Raleigh Tavern, was made about 1740 to 1750.

Glass 20¼″ x 27¼″; over-all size 28¾″ x 46½″
$375

CWLG 9

The symmetry of mature Chippendale style is perfected in this fine mahogany mirror. The original was made in Philadelphia between 1756 and 1762, and may be seen today in the George Wythe House in Williamsburg.

Glass 12½″ x 21¾″; over-all size 18¾″ x 35¼″
$210

CWLG 8

A gilded rosette of stylized leaves ornaments this delicate Chippendale mirror. The reproduction is an exact copy of an English mahogany antique, made about 1760, now hanging in the King's Arms Tavern in Williamsburg. Glass 15½" x 27¼"; over-all size 22" x 42¼" $285

CWLG 6

This magnificent Queen Anne looking glass is a faithful copy of an original dating from the reign of George I. The entire frame is made of rich gilded gesso, and is decorated with a carved shell and two eagle heads. Glass 16½" x 28½"; over-all size 22¼" x 41" $310

These two handsome mirrors, adaptations of antiques in the Williamsburg collection, may be seen also on pages 50 and 51.

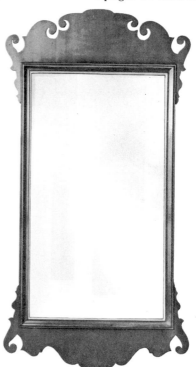

WA 1032

The antique American looking glass which inspired this graceful adaptation hangs today in the Raleigh Tavern in Williamsburg. The mahogany adaptation has the soft curves of the original Chippendale piece made between 1750 and 1775. Glass 15¼" x 27¼"; over-all size 21½" x 40¾" $140

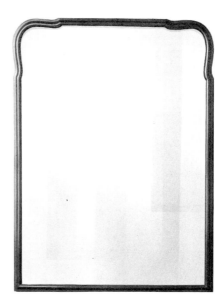

CWLG 12

A faithful copy of a rare Queen Anne design, this beveled-edge looking glass is beautifully proportioned to a small scale. The English antique, made between 1700 and 1720, hangs in the Governor's Palace. Cutting and polishing by hand the intricate curves of this beveled edge require the skill of a master craftsman. Virginia Metalcrafters makes the graceful brass sconce. Over-all size 6½" x 24"   Disc.

CWLG 2

The convex glass of this Federal-style mirror is framed in gilt wood and gesso. Probably made in America in the very late eighteenth century, the original now hangs in the Williamsburg Inn. Two candle arms balance a fiery eagle with outspread arms.

Glass diameter 11¾"; over-all size 17½" x 38¾" $435

WA 1028

This Queen Anne mirror is an adaptation of a looking glass made in England about 1710 and now in the Colonial Williamsburg collection. The pleasing simplicity of the original has been faithfully kept in this contemporary piece.

Glass 21¼" x 29½"; over-all size 23½" x 31½"
Mahogany frame $115
Gold frame   125

In this stunning room an antique ivory Raleigh Tavern spread is used on the CW 58 Bed (page 39). Accenting the classic design in the bedcover is the handsome fabric-wallpaper coordinate, Floral Stripe (page 72).

Photograph courtesy Morgan-Jones.

Williamsburg BEDSPREADS

Morgan-jones, weaver of highest quality textiles for almost a century, has reproduced for Craft House two handsome bedspreads based on antiques in the Williamsburg collection. These authentic reproductions faithfully copy the original rich designs and colors; they are available also in a variety of exciting adaptation colors.

◄─◄ RALEIGH TAVERN

Copied in detail from a textile in the Williamsburg collection, the Raleigh Tavern bedspread has a design of alternating rows of ribbed squares and rosettes. It is a variation of a four-harness overshot weave, a type of fabric often made and used in colonial homes. Four-inch fringe decorates three sides of this charming 100% cotton bedspread. It is available in the glowing colors shown below.

Twin 79″ x 110″ $23.85
Double 94″ x 110″ $26.50

QUEEN ANNE

This handsome all-cotton bedspread has been copied from an Italian or Spanish spread of the eighteenth century. The elaborate flower-and-leaf design of the original has been faithfully reproduced in this luxurious brocatelle, and a thick fringe is used on three sides. It is machine-washable, pre-shrunk, and needs no ironing. The document color is Palace Gold. It is also available in Antique Ivory and York Blue, as shown on the chart below.

Twin 81″ x 110″ $46.35
Double 96″ x 110″ $51.50

Raleigh Tavern   (a)   (b)   (c)   (d)   (e)   (f)   (g)

(a) Colonial Copper
(b) Dominion Blue
(c) Crown Gold
(d) Hearth Red
(e) Boxwood Green
(f) Snow White
(g) Teal Blue
Also, Antique Ivory
(see picture opposite)

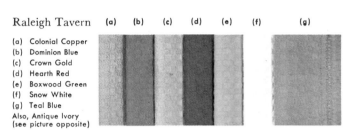

Queen Anne   (a)   (b)   (c)

(a) York Blue
(b) Antique Ivory
(c) Palace Gold

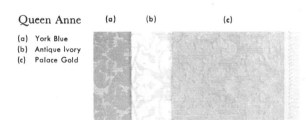

A Queen Anne bedspread in York Blue is the outstanding feature of this exciting contemporary bedroom. An unusual idea here is the use of a single bedspread as a coverlet on a double bed (CW 139, page 38).   *Photograph courtesy Morgan-Jones.*

Williamsburg FABRICS by Schumacher

Williamsburg fabrics, produced for Craft House by F. Schumacher and Company of New York, include more than 45 patterns in some 250 color variations. Most of these are authentic reproductions of antique fabrics used in Colonial Williamsburg; others commemorate the life and art of eighteenth-century Williamsburg.

The rich colors, patterns, and textures of *Williamsburg* fabrics reflect an age when English looms were producing a dazzling variety of textiles. The women of colonial Virginia introduced these elegant fabrics into their homes, using the bold combinations of color and pattern now exhibited in the restored homes and public buildings of Colonial Williamsburg.

Today's homes—whether furnished with antiques, with *Williamsburg* Furniture Reproductions, or with pieces of modern design—can be given the same dramatic flair with a creative use of *Williamsburg* fabrics. The choice is abundant; the combinations are limitless; the quality is superb.

bosite page, left to right:

*WYTHE HOUSE FLORAL

Two eighteenth-century textile designs have been united to make this fine cotton fabric. It has an over-all pattern of thorny stems bearing flowers, leaves, and buds; and side borders of alternate flowers and stripes. The coordinate wallpaper may be seen on page 76.

Width 48″ $9.60 per yard

DOBBY WEAVE

An excellent fabric for many purposes, Dobby Weave cotton is treated with stain-resistant Zepel. It is a copy of an old American diaper design, and is available in a wide range of colors.

Width 54″ $4.50 per yard

*APPLES

Copied from an eighteenth-century quilt lining, this fabric has narrow stripes and stylized apples on a natural background. It has been reproduced in linen (shown here) and adapted in a woven cotton (see page 69). The matching wallpaper may be seen on page 77.

†Woven cotton: width 54″
                    $13.15 per yard
Printed linen: width 48″
                    $7.50 per yard

FLORIBUNDA

This handsome cotton has been reproduced from an eighteenth-century fabric of French origin. It has a pattern of undulating stems bearing tulips, carnations, morning glories, roses, and other flowers.

Width 36″; repeat 30½″
                    $6.00 per yard

*†BOMBAY

The design of this rich cotton print was inspired by a book or lining paper from an eighteenth-century collection. A coordinated wallpaper is also available, as described on page 77.

Width 36″ $4.50 per yard

All fabrics are available in a choice of colorations.

Above:

WYTHE HOUSE BORDER RESIST

This fine cotton fabric has a repeat pattern of large leaves and sunflowers with a two inch border of trailing vines. Copied from a mid-eighteenth-century textile, resist-dyed in two shades of blue, it is shown here as it is used in a bedroom of the George Wythe House. The border of the fabric has been used to outline the valances and draperies in this set of window and bed hangings.

Width 50″; repeat 28″ $6.15 per yard

Right:

*POTPOURRI

A piece of antique block-printed cotton made in England has been copied in this charming reproduction fabric. Matching dinnerware by Wedgwood and wallpaper by Katzenbach & Warren are also available (pages 72, 75, and 115).

Width 36″; repeat 22¼″ $7.15 per yard

Color samples of all *Williamsburg* fabrics are available upon request: cotton samples (2″ x 6″) ten cents per pattern with full color range included; damask samples (3″ x 6″) fifty cents deposit per sample. Large samples of all fabrics are also available; a deposit equivalent to the price per yard is requested. All deposits are refunded when samples are returned.

†Adaptation.
*Also available in matching wallpaper.

WILLIAMSBURG SILK FABRICS

Above, left to right:

POMEGRANATE DAMASK

This elegant silk fabric has a rich pattern of large symmetrical plant forms and giant curling leaves. It is a copy of a typical damask design of about 1700.

Width 50″; repeat 32″   Discontinued

†*Williamsburg* SATIN

Available in many colors, this luxurious satin is copied from a number of examples in the Williamsburg collection.

Width 50″ $30.00 per yard

LUDWELL DAMASK

A floral pattern with a central framed bouquet is woven into this handsome damask. The document color of this early- to mid-eighteen-century design is reproduced in pure silk; adaptation colors, including the coloration illustrated above, are in cotton.

Silk (blue only): width 50″; repeat 17½″ $51.75 per yard
†Cotton: width 53″; repeat 18½″ $16.50 per yard

PALACE SUPPER ROOM LAMPAS

A basket of naturalistic flowers alternates with a vase of blossoms in this silk lampas used in the Governor's Palace. The original fabric is probably French, woven about 1775.

Width 50″; repeat 55″ $85.50 per yard

†Adaptation

Williamsburg VELVET

Glowing colors and exquisite texture are combined in this fine silk velvet, a fabric of unusual elegance. Like the original, the reproduction silk pile is backed with cotton.

Width 50″ $33.75 per yard

BRUTON DAMASK

A rich silk fabric, this damask has a repeating central design of flowers framed with a foliate cartouche. Also available as an adaptation fabric in silk and cotton.

Silk: width 50″; repeat 23½″ $49.50 per yard
†Silk and cotton: width 52″; repeat 23½″ $23.25 per yard

Williamsburg TAFFETA

Threads of two colors are used to weave this fine silk fabric. The result is a pleasing changeable effect. The reproduction is available in more than 15 colors.

Width 50″ $21.75 per yard

LORD DUNMORE DAMASK

Reproduced in silk, and adapted in rayon and silk (as shown here), this damask has a pattern of undulating floral boughs framing individual flower motifs.

Silk (blue only): width 50″; repeat 18″ $49.15 per yard
'†Rayon and silk: width 53″; repeat 23½″ $25.90 per yard

GLOUCESTER DAMASK

Stylized leaves and flowers are arranged in a symmetrical pattern in this fine silk damask, copied from a seventeenth-century design. It is illustrated again on pages 24 and 25.

Width 50″; repeat 28¾″ $56.65 per yard

Above, left to right:

All fabrics are available in a choice of colorations.

FLOWERING TREE

Copied from an antique English quilt, this fine glazed chintz has a repeating pattern of undulating branches bearing peonies, roses, tulips, and poppies, as well as a variety of leaves.
Width 54″; repeat 34″ $10.35 per yard

*BLUEBELL STRIPE

A stripe of diamonds alternates with a trailing vine of bluebells in this dainty cotton fabric. The original English design was a copperplate printed about 1770. The reproduction has been treated with Zepel. A coordinate wallpaper is illustrated on page 74.
Width 36″ $6.60 per yard

*FLOWERED PRINT

Like the antique (*ca.* 1780) French fabric, this gay cotton has an over-all design of vine-like stems bearing berries, leaves, and exotic flowers. The matching wallpaper is illustrated on page 81.
Width 36″; repeat 14½″ $6.40 per yard

POMEGRANATE RESIST

A large pattern of pomegranate flowers and feathery leaves, copied from an eighteenth-century resist-dyed design, lends drama to this linen and cotton fabric. It is used to upholster the sofa pictured on page 17.
Width 50″; repeat 20½″ $7.45 per yard

*COUNTRY LINEN

This fine-quality linen is available in a wide range of exciting colors. Its weave is copied from an American antique textile. A coordinate wallpaper is pictured on page 80.
Width 50″ $6.75 per yard

*RALEIGH TAVERN RESIST

Shown here covering a WA 1011 Chair, this linen and cotton fabric has a pattern of floral bouquets alternating with a ribbon entwined with fruit and flowers. Its coordinate wallpaper is described on pages 72 and 78; it is used for draperies in the bedroom scene on page 63.
Width 50″; repeat 42″ $10.15 per yard

*Also available in matching wallpaper.

Above, left to right:

All fabrics are available in a choice of colorations.

§Carriages

This commemorative cotton fabric shows carriages used in Williamsburg: the Randolph Coach, Blue Phaeton, Wythe Chariot, and a Diligence.

Width 36″; repeat 18½″ $5.25 per yard

Floral Trails

The design on this fine cotton, copperplate-printed in England about 1770, has an unusual quality of needlework. Graceful vines bear crocuses, roses, daisies, bachelor's buttons, lilies, and thistles.

Width 54″; repeat 32″ $8.70 per yard

Plantation Calico

This pattern, influenced by Indian designs of exotic plants and flowers, was copied from a French document of the late eighteenth century. The fabric is cotton.

Width 50″; repeat 13¼″ $8.80 per yard

Ribbon Stripe

Copied from a late-eighteenth-century French design, this intricate pattern of undulating stripes, floral sprigs, and bouquets is elegant in cotton.

Width 50″; repeat 15½″ $9.25 per yard

Taffeta Linen

An eighteenth-century linen sheet was copied to make this excellent fabric. It is available in many stunning colors.

Width 50″ $6.90 per yard

*Tulip

Stylized tulips arranged in small geometric patterns cover this handsome woven cotton fabric. The design follows a seventeenth-century document. The matching wallpaper is described on pages 72 and 80.

Width 50″ $19.15 per yard

Left:

*Multi-Stripe

Striped patterns were popular in the late eighteenth century. This chevron twill design in cotton is shown here at the window of the Brush-Everard House dining room. Katzenbach & Warren has produced a coordinate wallpaper (page 76).

Width 50″ $10.15 per yard

*Also available in matching wallpaper.
§Commemorative

Above, left to right:

WYTHE HOUSE STRIPE

Balance and simplicity distinguish this handsome cotton fabric. The two-tone red shown above is the document color.

Width 50″ $9.00 per yard

FLORAL BOUGH

The plain background of this cotton is splashed with large blossoms of iris, roses, chrysanthemums, lilies, lilacs, carnations, and passion flowers borne on a gnarled, undulating stem. The antique, a fine French copperplate design, and the reproduction fabrics are used in the Wythe House. The sofa on page 2 has a slipcover of this fabric.

Width 36″; repeat 29½″ $6.40 per yard

*APPLES

Shown here in the woven cotton adaptation, this symmetrical design is also available as an exact reproduction in printed linen (page 65). A coordinate wallpaper can be seen on page 77.

†Woven cotton: width 54″ $13.15 per yard

Printed linen: width 48″ $7.50 per yard

GRAPES

One of the oldest and most popular of the *Williamsburg* reproduction fabrics, this cotton has stripes of grapes, vines, and leaves, alternating with a stripe of small flower-and-leaf design. The original is English, block-printed in about 1790.

Width 36″; repeat 16½″ $6.40 per yard

*Also available in matching wallpaper.

§Commemorative

†Adaptation   *All fabrics are available in a choice of colorations.*

§MONUMENTS OF WILLIAMSBURG

This commemorative pattern shows some of Williamsburg's important buildings: Wren Building, Capitol, Palace, Ludwell-Paradise House, Raleigh Tavern. The fabric is cotton.

Width 36″; repeat 30″   Discontinued

69

WILDFLOWERS

Bunches of flowers, leaves, and buds in a trailing serpentine pattern cover this lovely cotton, copied from a late-eighteenth-century French fabric. A matching dinnerware pattern by Wedgwood is pictured on page 115.

Width 50″; repeat 31″ $9.40 per yard

SOLOMON'S SEAL

Graceful flowers, among them roses, carnations, and Solomon's seal, spring from thorny stems in this fine cotton pattern. The antique was printed at Bromley Hall factory, Middlesex, England, about 1775. Today it is used in the Brush-Everard House.

Width 40″; repeat 35½″ $5.85 per yard

BELLFLOWER

Full-blown flowers alternate with a stripe of half-open bellflower blossoms entwined with leaves and a ribbon to make a handsome fabric, produced in a linen-cotton combination. The sofa on page 42 is upholstered in this pattern.

Width 50″; repeat 14″ $10.90 per yard

HORSE AND FOX →

This cotton reproduction is shown here as it is used in a Wythe House bedroom. Animal vignettes are united by an arborescent branch in this pattern, first printed in England about 1770.

Width 36″; repeat 37″ $6.40 per yard

*Also available in matching wallpaper.

LIVERPOOL BIRDS

Fanciful and imaginary birds were popular eighteenth-century decorative motifs. They were the inspiration for this fine cotton.

Width 54″; repeat 7″ $11.65 per yard

NOSEGAY

This airy design on cotton has small bouquets framed by twig-like stems. It is copied from a French design of the eighteenth century.

Width 36″; repeat 14″ $7.00 per yard

*CHECKS

A satisfying and endlessly useful design, this small check is copied from an American antique document. It is made of linen and cotton. See the matching wallpaper described on page 79.

Width 48″ $7.15 per yard

All fabrics are available in a choice of coloration

Coverlet Cotton. A sturdy fabric with a decided pattern in the weave, Coverlet Cotton is reproduced from an American antique bedcovering.

Width 52″ $13.90 per yard

Randolph Texture. A blend of cotton, silk, and rayon, its heavy weight is particularly suitable for upholstery and draperies.

Width 54″ $16.15 per yard

Drysdale Twill. A silk and rayon combination, this plain weave comes in strong exciting colors. It is an excellent choice for draperies.

Width 54″ $25.50 per yard

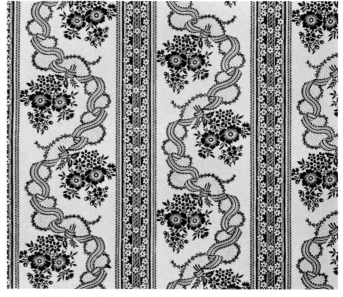

Above: *FLORAL STRIPE

Bouquets tied with ribbon alternate with wide stripes of stylized flowers in this reproduction of an eighteenth-century French cotton fabric. See pages 72 and 75 for a description of its matching wallpaper.

Width 36″; repeat 12½″ $6.00 per yard

All fabrics are available in a choice of colorations.

JONES TOILE

This printed cotton fabric is a reproduction of an English textile made in 1761 by Robert Jones in his Old Ford factory in London. The legends "R. JONES/1761" and "R.I. & Co./Old Ford/1761" are an unobtrusive part of the design. Summer hangings for the Palace ballroom are made of this stunning cotton.

Width 40″; repeat 77″ $7.35 per yard

*SPOTSWOOD

Shown here adapted in woven cotton in numerous rich colors, this symmetrical design of scrolls and stylized flowers is also reproduced as a silk and cotton fabric in the original blue and gold combination. The antique is probably seventeenth-century Spanish. A coordinate wallpaper is shown on page 74.

Width 54″; repeat 8¾″
†Cotton: $14.65 per yard
Silk and cotton
    $33.00 per yard

*Also available in matching wallpaper
†Adaptation

Williamsburg FABRIC AND WALLPAPER COORDINATES

F. SCHUMACHER & COMPANY AND KATZENBACH & WARREN have produced for the Reproductions Program an exciting group of *Williamsburg* fabric-wallpaper coordinates. This contemporary decorative idea was inspired by the eighteenth-century practice of using wallpaper designs for fabrics and copying fabric patterns in wallpaper.

Listed below is this collection of handsome coordinated fabrics and wallpapers, with the pages on which they are described.

	Wallpaper price per single roll	Wallpaper described on page	Fabric price per yard	Fabric described on page
Bluebell Stripe	$5.10	74	$6.60	67
Bombay	5.10	77	4.50	65
Country Linen	4.80	80	6.75	67
Floral Stripe	5.10	75	6.00	71
Flowered Print	6.00	81	6.40	67
Multi-Stripe	5.10	76	10.15	68
Potpourri	6.00	75	7.15	65
Raleigh Tavern	5.10	78	10.15	67
Spotswood Damask	5.40	74	14.65	71
Tulip	5.10	80	18.00	68
Williamsburg Apples	5.10	77	13.15	69
Williamsburg Check	5.40	79	7.15	70
Wythe House Floral	6.00	76	9.60	65

POTPOURRI

FLORAL STRIPE

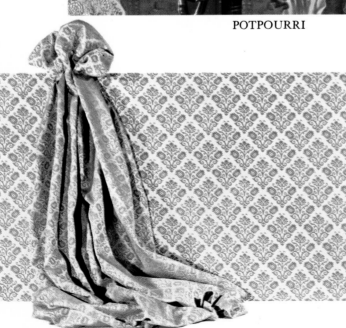

TULIP

RALEIGH TAVERN

COLONIAL WILLIAMSBURG Window & Bed Hangings

by ERNEST LoNANO

VISITORS to Williamsburg often express interest in the window and bed hangings in the Exhibition Buildings. They notice that the curators of Colonial Williamsburg use different types of eighteenth-century fabrics in many patterns and a variety of valance and curtain treatments.

Those who wish to re-create the effect of Williamsburg interiors face the problem of where and how to begin. The following discussion of the approach to window and bed hangings by the curatorial staff of Colonial Williamsburg may offer suggestions of interest. Examples have been drawn both from the eighteenth-century exhibition rooms and from the display rooms at Craft House, where materials reproduced or adapted from those of the eighteenth century may be examined and ordered.

SELECTING FABRICS

At Colonial Williamsburg every fabric and every design used for window and bed hangings has a precedent in the eighteenth century. That is, surviving eighteenth-century textiles or hangings are available for copying or actual use; or drawings, prints, and paintings of the period are studied to document the design; and such sources as newspaper advertisements and the accounts of merchants are analyzed for references to the use of fabrics. There are no precise rules for the selection of fabrics, but some basic considerations must be followed.

The room to be decorated—a bedroom, dining room, sitting room, etc.—may determine the choice. Equally important is the mood of the room: formal or informal, simple or elegant. Silk material enhances the elegance of a formal or elaborate decor. Cotton, wool, or linen may be used for this effect or in a simpler room.

Size of the room is another consideration. Fabrics with a pattern bold in color or large in scale are usually the most suitable for large rooms, those of small design and subtle color for smaller rooms. Even the type, size, and number of windows in a room may influence the choice of design: many hangings in a small space call for restraint in the design; few hangings in a larger room allow a bolder approach.

WINDOW TREATMENTS

The proportions of windows, their placement in a room, and the dimensions of a room itself are factors to consider. They may determine whether to employ shaped valances, festoons, shirred valances, jabots, etc.

Equally important is the matter of mood. Festoons and jabots are suitable for a formal room. Simpler treatments, such as shaped valances, are appropriate for less elaborate decor.

Visitors to Williamsburg see three basic formal treatments. One consists of festoons and jabots over floor-length curtains. Particularly effective with high windows, this treatment requires fabric with a large pattern for display in the festoon. At Williamsburg proportions are maintained by the use of only two festoons to a window, each festoon of two feet or less. This formula is followed because windows at Williamsburg are only approximately three and one-half feet wide.

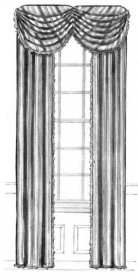

FIGURE 1   FIGURE 2

FIGURE 3   FIGURE 4

The number of folds in the festoon influences the sense of formality: many folds give the appearance of depth and richness, fewer folds provide a lighter visual effect and seem less formal. Curtains tied back in this kind of treatment make the windows look shorter and wider. A fringe adds elegance to their treatment as in the Craft House dining room where it appears on both festoons and jabots (Fig. 1), or in the Brush-Everard House dining room where it occurs with the festoons alone (Fig. 2).

A second formal treatment in Williamsburg consists of festoons with longer jabots, usually to the window sill or the chair rail. These may be used in place of floor-length curtains. An example can be seen in the Daphne Room of the Raleigh Tavern (Fig. 3) and the Wythe House hall (Fig. 4). These effectively complement the architectural features of the rooms, for they extend to the break in wall height created by the chair rail or dado. This type of treatment also is functional. It keeps the hangings up and away from the floor in an area difficult to maintain or frequently used in a household.

The third basic formal treatment can be seen in the state dining room of the Governor's Palace (Fig. 5). Here an elaborately shaped valance with three deep scallops displays to advantage the large pattern of the

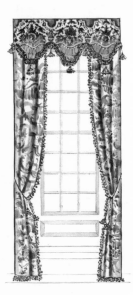

FIGURE 5   FIGURE 6

fabric. In this instance the design, or repeat, determines the depth of the valance. The northeast bedroom of the Wythe House (Fig. 6), the Craft House living room (Fig. 7), and the Wythe House northwest bedroom (Fig. 8) all show examples of shaped valances, the first with plain fabric, the other two taking full advantage of the fabric design.

In less formal treatments, valances usually are similar to those found in more formal settings, but they are simpler in design and customarily include curtains to the floor. The winter draperies in the Wythe House northwest bedroom (Fig. 9) are an example of a simple valance made from a cotton fabric informal in nature. Another example appears in the southeast bedroom of the same house where the design of a block-printed resist helped to determine the shape of the valance (Fig. 10). The use of cotton and a free, bold pattern make the more detailed shape of the valance appear less formal.

FIGURE 7   FIGURE 8

Shaped valances with curtains to the sill can be seen in many rooms at Williamsburg. This treatment often solves the problem of dormer windows or other small windows which need not be neglected because of their size. Properly treated, they can enhance the decor of a room. The Brush-Everard House southwest bedroom includes shaped valances (Fig. 11), and another treatment is represented by the valances in one of the Raleigh Tavern bedrooms (Fig. 12). The last type of valance is the simplest to make, and the effect can be heightened with trimmings.

TRIMMINGS

The type of fabric used and the desired effect offer guides for the selection of trimmings. Where possible, both should be of the same material: silk fabric, silk fringe; linen fabric, linen trimming, etc. Depth of the trimming should be proportionate to the depth of the valance or festoon, and normally both the valance and the curtains are trimmed.

A consistent use of trimming on valance and curtain is especially important on damask. On a solid color,

FIGURE 9   FIGURE 10

either a fringe or binding is often applied at the bottom of the valance and the front and bottom of the curtains (Fig. 6). A binding or braid may be applied at the edge of the valance (Fig. 8) or set in approximately the width of the trim on the faces of valances and curtains. If the binding or braid is raised it usually is more elaborate than a fringe or trim at the edges. Fringe may be used with all fabrics. To enhance a cotton or linen print, fringe of the same texture and color as the fabric is the most effective (Figs. 2, 3, 12). In fact, any trimming should relate to a predominant color in the fabric, as in the Wythe House northwest bedroom (Fig. 8). A multi-color fringe can even be used with a material of many colors.

An interesting effect can be achieved by using the border of a fabric for trimming, as in the Wythe House southeast bedroom. Short draperies can be trimmed with a printed binding related to the fabric design, as in the Brush-Everard House southwest bedroom (Fig. 11).

A final word on trimming: There is no obligation to trim every curtain. The mood in a room should govern the decision to use, or not to use, trimming.

HOW HIGH? HOW WIDE?

When fabric has been chosen and treatment has been decided on, there still may be other factors to consider.

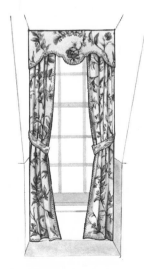

FIGURE 11   FIGURE 12

Is all possible light needed from the window? Are there Venetian blind boxes at the window tops to be covered? How high should the curtains be hung, and how far on either side should they extend?

If light is a consideration, the window treatment must be as high as possible and must permit the curtains to cover the side members of the window frame without encroaching on the window panes. It is important to proper window treatment that the valance cover everything at the top of the window and that, without becoming disproportionately deep, it extend up to or close to the ceiling or molding.

A good rule in determining the depth of a valance is to allow 1½ or 1¾ inches at the deepest point for every foot in over-all length of the window treatment. This rule varies slightly according to the fabric used. With a fabric of a light color, a valance may be deeper than with material of a dark color, because it will seem smaller in scale. As we have already observed, the pattern of a fabric may also govern the shape of a valance.

Another factor to consider is the fullness of curtains. What is called 100 per cent fullness gives the most pleasing effect; that is, if the window is four feet wide the material for curtains should be eight feet wide. Most fabrics measure approximately 50 inches in width. Therefore, a pair of curtains for a window four feet wide require two widths, one for each curtain.

In dormers, the windows themselves regulate the hanging of curtains. Deep dormers with shallow sills permit a variation from normal procedure, namely curtains set away from the sill and hanging to the floor.

BED HANGINGS

On a properly dressed bed, the hangings should bear an obvious relationship to the window treatment. For example, the valance at the top of canopy beds and field beds should have the same shape as the window valance. This relationship gives a room the visual unity of the upstairs bedrooms of the Wythe House as well as the Craft House display bedrooms.

Gathered or shirred valances usually are more appropriate on the canopies of field beds, for they create a light and informal effect. The shirred valance can also be used over windows. If shirred dimity is used at the bed, a print can serve at the windows and the valance be shaped.

Authenticity demands that beds in the Williamsburg exhibition bedrooms support three pairs of curtains. At the bottom of the bed, below the rail, a straight or shaped valance or a gathered ruffle should be used. Valances at the top and bottom of the foot of a bed should, of course, be of the same shape.

Finally, dressing a bed properly requires a careful consideration of the bedspread. It may be of the same textile as the bed and window hangings or complement them. If the hangings are of a printed material, the spread can be of a solid color which matches a color of the print. Should a fabric of a solid color be used, the bedspread can be enhanced with quilting.

Typical Valance Designs used in Colonial Williamsburg

A. A soft-shaped valance of regular and inverted scallops. This relatively informal design calls for a small-patterned or figured fabric.

B. A more formal valance than A, and more suitable for a fabric with a large design.

C. "Dog ear" valance, an English design. It is suited to fabrics with an over-all or flowing pattern.

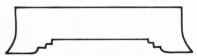

D. A more formal "dog ear" valance with an oriental motif in its pagoda shape. The design is used in the Wythe House parlor and is most appropriate for a formal fabric.

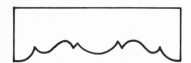

E. A Chippendale-type design. This valance is suitable with a large-patterned formal fabric.

F. A design in the European style. Large-patterned fabrics are suitable here.

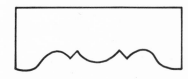

G. A transitional shape. This valance is adaptable to most fabrics, whether the design is an over-all or a definite pattern.

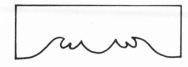

H. A versatile design taken from an antique in the Williamsburg collection. It is suitable for a plain or small-patterned fabric.

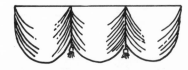

I. Soft festoons calling for a damask or similar formal fabric. The shape is influenced by French designs of the eighteenth century.

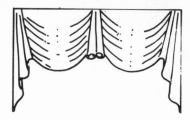

J. A treatment similar to Jefferson's sketches of hangings at Monticello. This festoon and jabot design is formal and best suited to damasks.

K. A less formal treatment using festoons alone. This valance design can be adapted to most fabrics.

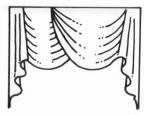

L. A very formal, heavily draped treatment with a French feeling. It is late-eighteenth-century and is most often used with damasks.

M. A single shirred valance. This simple, easy-to-make design is appropriate for any informal fabric.

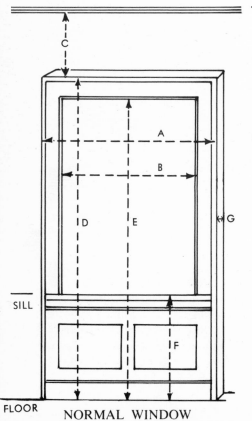

NORMAL WINDOW

CORRECT METHOD FOR MEASURING THE MOST USUAL KINDS OF WINDOWS

A. EXTREME WIDTH   D. EXTREME HEIGHT
B. INSIDE WIDTH   E. INSIDE HEIGHT
C. TOP OF TRIM TO CEILING   F. SILL TO FLOOR
G. RETURN

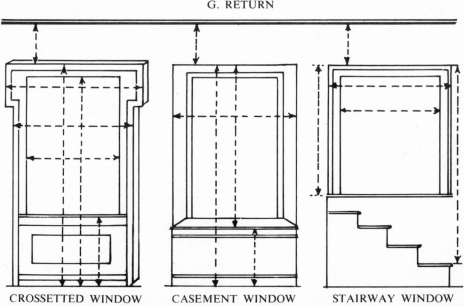

CROSSETTED WINDOW   CASEMENT WINDOW   STAIRWAY WINDOW

WILLIAMSBURG WALLPAPERS

by Katzenbach and Warren

THE Colonial Williamsburg collection of fine antique furniture and furnishings includes numerous eighteenth-century wallpaper fragments, discovered in the lining of old trunks and dispatch boxes, or under layers of modern paint and paper on the walls of colonial buildings. The skilled craftsmen of Katzenbach and Warren have copied a number of Colonial Williamsburg's rare documents to produce these exquisite *Williamsburg* Wallpaper Reproductions. Each design has been accurately reproduced in the colors of the original, as well as in a wide range of other color combinations.

In addition to the authentic reproductions, wallpapers commemorating Williamsburg art and life are available in a number of colorations. A selection of wallpapers with coordinate fabrics is listed on page 72.

Most *Williamsburg* wallpapers are manufactured with a protective stain-resistant coating for carefree use in bathroom, kitchen, and nursery, and are pretrimmed for ease in hanging.

A large wallpaper catalogue will be sent on loan for a $6.00 deposit plus $.75 mailing charge. Deposit will be refunded if the catalogue is returned within 30 days. For those who wish to keep the catalogue there is an additional charge of $12.00.

Please note that although wallpaper is priced by the single roll it is packed only in double rolls or triple rolls.

The Ducks

SUPPER ROOM COMMEMORATIVE WALLPAPER

The Doves

THIS PAPER is a superb adaptation by Katzenbach and Warren of the magnificent Chinese wallpaper in the Governor's Palace supper room. The antique paper, hand-painted in the mid-eighteenth century, has been reduced in scale and a few panels have been eliminated in order to suit the homes of today. All the grace and color of the original are captured in this commemorative design, and most of the details of the old paper have been carefully copied. For instance, all of the birds are in pairs, except for the owl who has no mate. Dragonflies, bees, a spider's web, a caterpillar, and even a few flies and mosquitoes have been artfully copied on this fine paper.

The two panels that make up the paper, "The Doves" and "The Ducks," (both shown above) are available printed on a wide range of ground colors.

This wallpaper is illustrated again on page 30. For additional information please write Craft House.

Single Panels   Each $90.00
One Duck and One Dove Panel   Set $180.00

WEST ST. MARY'S MANOR

This graceful pattern is copied from a mid-eighteenth-century paper originally used in West St. Mary's Manor, a colonial Maryland home. The ribbon-like bands that simulate lace are often found in fabrics of this period.

$5.10 per single roll (sold in double rolls)

†AVIARY

Adapted from a linen handkerchief entitled "The Aviary or Bird Fancyers Recreation," this charming wallpaper illustrates about a dozen birds with notes on their habits and care. The original design was copperplate-printed about 1770.

$6.00 per single roll (sold in triple rolls)

*†BLUEBELL STRIPE

This wallpaper with its dainty motif of stripes and trailing vines of bluebells is an adaptation of a fabric in an eighteenth-century English quilt. For the fabric reproduction, see page 67.

$5.10 per single roll (sold in double rolls)

*†SPOTSWOOD DAMASK

Symmetrical scrolls and stylized flowers make up the design of this elegant wallpaper copied from the seventeenth-century Spanish silk document. The fabric coordinate is illustrated on page 71.

$5.40 per single roll (sold in triple rolls)

Adaptation
*Also available in matching fabric

STENCIL SQUARE

Copied from a fragment in the Williamsburg collection, this handsome wallpaper is available in the document colors of blue on taupe, as well as in other rich combinations. Its simple geometric designs are particularly suitable for today's homes.

$4.80 per single roll
(sold in double rolls)

The Stencil Square pattern is shown here in a stair hall in Williamsburg.

*† POTPOURRI

Adapted from the cotton fabric of the same design (see page 65), this exciting pattern is rich with birds, flowers, and fruits. A dinnerware pattern by Wedgwood has also been inspired by this popular design.

$6.00 per single roll
(sold in double rolls)

All wallpapers are available in a choice of colorations.

†*FLORAL STRIPE

This rich design has been adapted from an eighteenth-century French textile and is available also in a reproduction fabric. Bouquets of flowers alternate with wide bands of tiny stylized flowers. It can be seen again on pages 62 and 72; the fabric on page 71.

$5.10 per single roll (sold in double rolls)

FLOWERED LACEWORK

The original of this beautiful pattern of meandering flowers and lacework ribbons was discovered in the castle of Count Alfred Potocki in Poland where it had been since about 1740. The paper, which bears a British tax stamp, was made in Holland and the design hand blocked in England.

$6.00 per single roll (sold in double rolls)

*Also available in matching fabric
†Adaptation

75

†*MULTI-STRIPE

This pattern, a popular design of the late eighteenth century, has been copied from an old fabric in the Williamsburg collection. A CW 14 Chair is shown here covered in a cotton reproduction which matches the wallpaper. See page 68 for the fabric.

$5.10 per single roll (sold in double rolls)

LAFAYETTE FLORAL

This charming floral pattern has been reproduced from an antique wallpaper fragment discovered in an eighteenth-century house in Kennebunkport, Maine and now in the Williamsburg collection. Designs of this type were popular also for silks and printed cottons of the period.

$6.00 per single roll (sold in double rolls)

†*WYTHE HOUSE FLORAL

The borders of the Wythe House Floral cotton (see page 64) inspired this graceful wallpaper pattern. In the wallpaper the borders combine for a striped effect; in the fabric they frame a large flowering vine.

$6.00 per single roll (sold in double rolls)

All wallpapers available in a choice of colorations.

§COLONIAL MOULDINGS

These papers were inspired by architectural features frequently found in the homes and buildings of eighteenth-century Virginia.

Cornice and Chair Rail (sold by the single roll containing 10 yards of cornice, 10 yards of chair rail, and 10 pairs of profile ends)

$12.00 per single roll

Wainscot (sold by the single roll containing 5 yards)

$12.00 per single roll

*Also available in matching fabric
§Commemorative
†Adaptation

§DUKE OF GLOUCESTER

Based on an eighteenth-century English textile, this commemorative pattern makes a fanciful and elegant wall covering. The vase and flowers were inspired by the lush floral arrangements used in the Governor's Palace, and the birds were copied from the Chinese wallpaper in the Palace supper room.

$5.10 per single roll
(sold in double rolls)

*†WILLIAMSBURG APPLES

A pattern of stripes and stylized apples from an eighteenth-century quilt lining has been adapted for this delightful wallpaper design. The matching fabric is shown on pages 65 and 69.

$5.10 per single roll
(sold in double rolls)

*BOMBAY

A rich pattern of leaves, vines, and flowers covers this unusual wallpaper, a reproduction of a book or lining paper of the eighteenth century. The matching fabric (see page 64) is shown here on the WA 1046 Chair.

$5.10 per single roll (sold in double rolls)

CHARLES II

The original paper from which this reproduction has been made dates from about 1660. Figures representing the four seasons surround a circle containing a lion and unicorn and the crowns of England, Scotland, and Ireland.

$6.00 per single roll (sold in double rolls)

BIRD AND ACORN

Copied from a book paper of about 1790, Bird and Acorn is available in the document colors of black on deep curry as well as other striking combinations for use in the homes of today.

$5.40 per single roll (sold in double rolls)

*Also available in matching fabric
§Commemorative
†Adaptation

DIAGONAL FLORAL

This pleasing design, shown here in white on putty, was copied from antique wallpaper found in an American house of the colonial period. The graceful ordered pattern is a charming background for any room.

$5.10 per single roll (sold in double rolls)

†HOMESPUN STRIPE

The textured pattern of this wallpaper was inspired by an eighteenth-century woolen blanket which was woven in America and is now in the Williamsburg collection. It is available in delightful soft colors.

$4.80 per single roll (sold in double rolls)

All wallpapers are available in a choice of colorations.

§ LITTLE CROWNS →
This commemorative paper was inspired by the crown of William III in whose honor the city of Williamsburg was named.

$3.90 per single roll
(sold in double rolls)

←RALEIGH TAVERN

Adapted from an antique French fabric, this dramatic wallpaper has a pattern of undulating ribbon stripes alternating with a bouquet of stylized flowers.

$5.10 per single roll
(sold in double rolls)

MANDARIN AND PINE TREE

A combination of English flowers and Oriental figures covers this rich reproduction wallpaper. The antique from which it was copied was originally used to line a truck, and dates from about 1760 to 1770. It is shown again on pages 10, 33, and 85.

$4.80 per single roll (sold in double rolls)

*Also available in matching fabric
§Commemorative
†Adaptation

78

MARY LLOYD

The original of this graceful floral design is a lining paper for an antique leather box. A label in the box identifies Mary Lloyd as a trunkmaker "at the corner of Pudding-Row, Opposite Winetavern Street, Dublin."

$4.80 per single roll (sold in double rolls)

§*WILLIAMSBURG* MILITARY

This novel and charming commemorative wallpaper design illustrates the historic buildings of Williamsburg together with regular Virginia troops and brightly uniformed English soldiers. See supplement for matching fabric.

$5.40 per single roll (sold in double rolls)

*Also available in matching fabric
§Commemorative
†Adaptation

*†*WILLIAMSBURG* CHECK

This pleasing design was taken from a linen tabby-weave fabric in the Williamsburg collection and is available in a variety of fresh and attractive colors. The fabric reproduction is described on page 70.

$5.40 per single roll (sold in double rolls)

CHINESE TILES

An interesting grouping of tiles is the subject of this reproduction of a mid-eighteenth-century wallpaper. It is of a type popularized by Thomas Chippendale and used by him in the decoration of several houses of that period.

$5.40 per single roll (sold in double rolls)

*†COUNTRY LINEN

Available in a number of rich colors, this textured wallpaper is coordinated with the fabric described on page 67. The document fabric is a linen grain bag of probable American origin.

$4.80 per single roll (sold in double rolls)

*†TULIP

This design of stylized flowers has been adapted from a Continental textile of the late seventeenth century. Charming and formal, it matches the fabric shown on page 68.

$5.10 per single roll
(sold in double rolls)

*All wallpapers (except Edenton)
are available in a choice of colorations.*

EDENTON

This rich pattern is a faithful copy of wallpaper found in the Joseph Hewes House in Edenton, North Carolina. The design was printed in the last quarter of the eighteenth century. Only the document color, as shown here, is available.

$36.00 per single roll
(sold in double rolls)

§ *WILLIAMSBURG* COMMEMORATIVE SCENIC

This handsome hand-printed paper consists of seven strips, each 27 inches wide trimmed, for a total width of 15 feet 9 inches. As illustrated below, and on page 81, the strips show Bruton Parish Church, the Governor's Palace, the Magazine and Guardhouse, the Courthouse of 1770, the Raleigh Tavern, and the Capitol. Not shown is the Garden, a filler strip which may be used anywhere to allow buildings or groups of buildings to be centered. Height of the patterns varies from $12\frac{1}{2}$ inches in the Garden to $22\frac{1}{4}$ inches in the Governor's Palace.

Individual strips $18.00
Set of seven strips $120.00

*Also available in matching fabric
§Commemorative
†Adaptation

WILLIAMSBURG COMMEMORATIVE SCENIC

BRUTON PARISH CHURCH   *THE GOVERNOR'S PALACE*   *THE MAGAZINE AND GUARDHOU*

†PALACE GARDEN DAMASK

This elegant wallpaper is copied from a fabric document of the second quarter of the eighteenth century. Benjamin Bucktrout, Williamsburg cabinetmaker, advertised paper hangings, including damask, for sale in the *Virginia Gazette* of May 9, 1771.

$6.00 per single roll (sold in triple rolls)

*†FLOWERED PRINT

Shown here with the matching cotton fabric, this gay and colorful paper has been adapted from a French block-printed textile made about 1780. For the fabric, please see page 67. $6.00 per single roll (sold in double rolls)

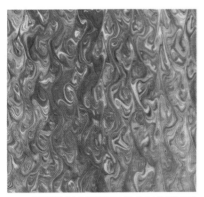

WILLIAMSBURG MARBLED
PAPERS (*Discontinued*)

FLORAL SQUARES →

This charming arrangement of floral squares is copied from a block-printed paper made in England about 1680. Used as a lining for a seventeenth-century Bible box, it is typical of papers found in boxes of the period.

$5.40 per single roll (sold in triple rolls)

*Also available in matching fabric
†Adaptation
All wallpapers are available in choice of colorations.

WILLIAMSBURG COMMEMORATIVE SCENIC (*Continued*)

THE COURTHOUSE OF 1770   *THE RALEIGH TAVERN*   *THE CAPITOL*

81

CW 128 Chair with
two NP 1 designs as upholstery.

Williamsburg
NEEDLE POINT

NEEDLEWORK in the eighteenth century was an art form as well as a housewife's diversion. Faithful copies in color and form of four handsome examples in the Colonial Williamsburg collection are now available for today's creative woman.

Imported from Belgium, each design has been worked in tramé or overlay to provide a color guide over which the piece may be finished.

Since each design is individually fabricated, canvas measurements may vary slightly. Therefore, when ordering, please state size of the piece to be covered. Crewel yarn for completing both the design and background is included with each order.

NP 1

NP 1 A lush design of carnations, tulips, and other flowers is already worked in petit point. The colors of the design are primarily soft greens, roses, and blues, and the background wool is a rich gold. Shown above on the CW 128 Chair, it is also suitable for a stool or pillow cover. Design 21½" x 13½"; canvas 35" x 23"

Not Available

NP 2 Often called the Pomegranate design because of its large central flower, this needle point shows a graceful grouping of carnations, roses, tulips, morning glory, pomegranate, and leaves. The colors are rich tones of red, yellow, blue, and green against a background of two tones of brown. It is appropriate for a chair seat or pillow cover. On page 23 the CW 147 Bench is shown upholstered in the NP 2. Design 17" x 18½"; canvas 28" x 30"   *Not Available*

NP 3 The central figure is a full-blown carnation, surrounded by roses, tulips, almond blossoms, cherry blossoms, and leaves. The colors are soft, clear shades of rose, cream, blue, and green; the background is in three shades of greenish blue. The CW 16 Chair, upholstered in the NP 3, is shown on page 29. Design 25½" x 21"; canvas 35" x 30" $107.55

NP 4 A floral and leaf design similar to NP 3, this pattern has a half-blown carnation as the central motif. Design 25½" x 21"; canvas 35" x 30" $107.55

NP 2

NP 3

NP 4

NP 23

COMMEMORATIVE NEEDLE POINT

Eᴀᴄʜ of these designs is handsome either in a frame; or as a cover for a chair seat, bench, or pillow; or as a fire-screen panel. Though not literal copies of antique needlework, Commemorative Needle Point designs were inspired by old pieces in the Colonial Williamsburg collection and by the art of the colonial period.

Each design has been worked in tramé, and tapestry yarn for completing the design is included. Yarn for the background is not, so that purchasers may select colors of their own choice.

NP 11 A floral arrangement in a basket is the design on this piece. The tramé is worked in pale shades of pink, lavender, and beige with highlights of bright reds and greens. Design 17″ x 15″; canvas 26″ x 26″
Not Available

NP 22 This design shows a natural floral arrangement with flowers in blue, green, rose, gold, and beige. It can be seen again on the WA 1016 Bench (page 50) and the CW 92 Fire Screen (page 22). Design 14″ x 10″; canvas 26″ x 19″
Not Available

NP 23 A bouquet is the motif for this design. The center flower is rose, with blues and greens predominating in the rest of the design. Design 10½″ x 10″; canvas 26″ x 22½″
Not Available

NP 71 A ribbon tied in a bow catches the bouquet in this design. The central figure is red; purple, green, and blue are among the other shades. Design 12½″ x 7½″; canvas 26″ x 21″
Not Available

NP 73 The floral motif in this piece is in soft shades of blue. A very balanced design, it is square with a triangle of three large flowers within it. Design 11″ x 10″; canvas 26″ x 23″
Not Available

NP 14 (not shown) A basket of flowers stands on a base in this design. Colors are lavender, rose, blues, yellows, and reds with green foliage. Parts of seven blossoms have been worked in petit point. Design 13¼″ x 16″; canvas 23″ x 26″
Not Available

NP 22

NP 73

NP 11

Williamsburg HAND-TINTED PRINTS
by THE DIETZ PRESS

ROBERT FURBER'S flower and fruit prints and Mark Catesby's bird prints, originally published in the early eighteenth century, have been faithfully reproduced by The Dietz Press for the modern connoisseur of fine prints. Though none of these three sets of prints was originally designed for decorative purposes, their exquisite detail and color have made them collectors' items since the time of their publication. Now once again available, the prints have been re-engraved on highest quality rag paper, and sensitively hand-tinted in exact reproduction of the original rich colors.

A different flower and fruit print is available for each month of the year. Please specify month desired.

For a complete listing of the twelve Catesby bird prints, see the Supplemental Price List.

Floral Prints

Unframed 18½″ x 24″ (including margins)	Each $10.30 Pair $19.30
Framed 18″ x 23″	Each $28.75 Pair $54.50

Fruit Prints

Unframed 18½″ x 24″ (including margins)	Each $10.30 Pair $19.30
Framed 20½″ x 26⅓″	Each $33.15 Pair $62.55

Bird Prints

Unframed 18″ x 24″ (including margins)
Each $10.30   Pair $19.30
Framed 18″ x 23″
Each $28.75   Pair $54.50

P 10 The Partridge Bird Print
Framed in black with gold-leaf trim

P 8 June Floral Print
Framed in black with gold-leaf trim

P 14 November Fruit Print
Framed in fruit wood with gold-leaf trim

This gracious Williamsburg dining room is lighted by a Governor's Office Chandelier (K 12939). On the hearth are elegant brass fireplace reproductions by the Harvin Company, including the CW 103-1 Firetools, the CW 100-1 Andirons, and the CW 102-1 Fender. The room is in the Robert Carter House, a privately occupied restored house of Colonial Williamsburg.

THE soft glow of candlelight is as pleasing to the modern homeowner as it was necessary to his eighteenth-century counterpart. On these pages are described chandeliers, sconces, and lanterns which may be used today as they were two hundred years ago to dispel the darkness. Each of these reproductions is a careful copy of a lighting fixture used in the restored buildings of Colonial Williamsburg, and in each case the character of the original has been faithfully preserved by the master craftsmen of Virginia Metalcrafters.

Available for use with candles, all fixtures have also been adapted to electricity to meet modern lighting requirements, conforming to Underwriters Specifications.

For complete information about chandeliers, please consult the Supplemental Price List.

K 12891
GOVERNOR'S PALACE CHANDELIER

Polished or antique pewter. Available with four lights (like the original), five lights or eight lights. Height 20″; width 28¾″; total length 44″ with 2 feet of suspension chain.

Four arms, electrified (shown)	$425
Four arms, candles	$380

Chandeliers and Hanging Lanterns

K 12894 APOTHECARY SHOP CHANDELIER

Polished or antique brass. Available with six lights (like the antique) or five lights. Height 18″; width 19″; total length 42″ with 2 feet of suspension chain.

Six arms, electrified (shown)	$415
Six arms, candles	$325

K 12895 RALEIGH TAVERN CHANDELIER

Polished or antique brass, or polished or antique pewter. Available with four lights (like the antique), five lights, or six lights. Height 18½″; width 22½″; total length 44″ with 3 suspension links.

Six arms, electrified, pewter (shown)	$455
Four arms, candles, pewter	$305

K 12939 GOVERNOR'S OFFICE CHANDELIER

Polished or antique brass. Two indirect lights inside base. Available only with eight arms (like the antique). Height 40″; width 32″; total length 52″ with 1 foot of suspension chain.

Eight arms, electrified (shown)	$855
Eight arms, candles	$755

K 12894

K 12895

K 12939

K 11751
BRUSH-EVERARD LANTERN
Polished or antique brass. Height 23″; width 10½″; total length 47″ with 2 feet of suspension chain.

Four lights, electrified $290
One light, candle $260

*K 11751S
BRUSH-EVERARD LANTERN, SMALL
Polished or antique brass. Height 16″; width 7½″; total length 40″ with 2 feet of suspension chain.

Three lights, electrified $240

K 12921
WATCHMAN'S LANTERN

Antique tin or antique brass. Height 21″; width 9″; total length 45″ with 2 feet of suspension chain.

Two lights, electrified,
brass or tin $280
Two lights, candles, tin $255

K 11758
TAYLOE HOUSE LANTERN

Polished brass or verdigris brass. Height 23″; width 10⅛″; total length 47″ with 2 feet of suspension chain.

Three lights, electrified $255
One light, candle $220

K 12893
GOVERNOR'S PALACE HALL LANTERN

Polished or antique brass. Beveled glass panels. Height 32″; width 9½″; total length 56″ with 2 feet of suspension chain.

Four lights, electrified $545
One light, candle $505

K 12892
GOVERNOR'S PALACE LANTERN

Polished or antique brass. Height 34″; width across corners 18″; total length 58″ with 2 feet of suspension chain.

Six lights, electrified $535
One light, candle $495

*K 12892S GOVERNOR'S PALACE LANTERN, SMALL
Polished or antique brass. Height 18″; width across corners 11″; total length 42″ with 2 feet of suspension chain. Not Shown.

Four lights, electrified $425

*Adaptation

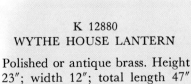

K 12880
WYTHE HOUSE LANTERN

Polished or antique brass. Height 23″; width 12″; total length 47″ with 2 feet of suspension chain.

Three lights, electrified $255
One light, candle $220

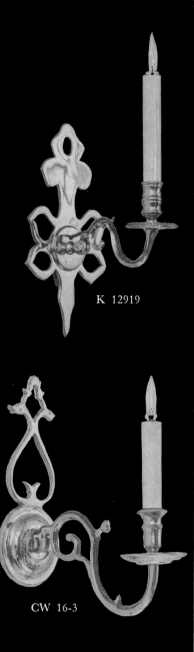

K 12919

CW 16-3

K 12919
GOVERNOR'S PALACE SCONCE
Polished or antique brass, or polished or antique pewter. Backplate height 11″; backplate width 5¾″; arm projects 7¾″.

Electrified	Brass $40.75;	pewter $50.75
Candle	Brass $33.25;	pewter $43.25

CW 16-3
PALACE WARMING ROOM SCONCE
Polished or antique brass. Backplate height 10½″; backplate width 4⅛″; arm projects 10⅝″.

Electrified	$48.50
Candle	$33.25

CW 16-22D
*DOUBLE-ARM BRUTON HURRICANE SCONCE
Same design and measurements as CW 16-22 Sconce but with double arms.

Electrified	With 10″ globes $97.50
Candles	With 10″ globes $82.50

CW 16-23
DOUBLE-ARM SCONCE
Polished or antique brass with handmade crystal globes. Total height with globes 17″; total width 15½″; backplate diameter 3⁵⁄₁₆″; arms project 9″. Available only for candles. $83.20

CW 16-22
BRUTON HURRICANE SCONCE
Polished or antique brass with handmade crystal globe. Total height with 10″ globe, 17″; with 13″ globe, 20″; backplate diameter 3¾″; arm projects 12″.

Electrified	With 10″ globe $56.50; with 13″ globe $61.50
Candle	With 10″ globe $46.50; with 13″ globe $51.50

CW 16-22SB
*SMOKE BELL
Glass smoke bell with brass arm that was designed to match the CW 16-22 Sconce

DISCONTINUED

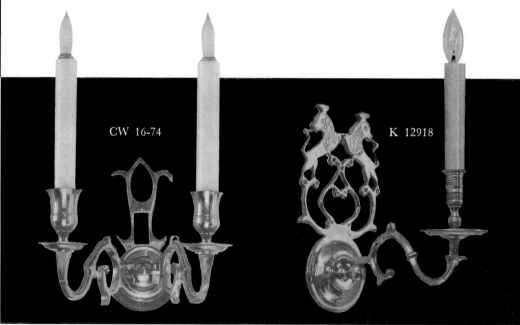

CW 16-22D

CW 16-23

CW 16-22SB

CW 16-74

K 12918

CW 16-22

CW 16-74
HOUSE OF BURGESSES SCONCE

Polished or antique brass, or polished or antique pewter. Backplate height 6¼″; backplate width 3¼″; arms project 7″. Mounted on walnut backplate when electrified.

Electrified	Brass $58.35;	pewter $68.35
Candle	Brass $45.75;	pewter $55.75

K 12918
CHOWNING'S TAVERN SCONCE

Polished or antique brass, or polished or antique pewter. Backplate height 10¾″; backplate width 5¾″; arm projects 10″.

Electrified	Brass $45.85;	pewter $55.85
Candle	Brass $33.25;	pewter $43.25

*Adaptation

K 12579

K 12579 PRINTING OFFICE CHANDELIER
Antique tin or tin painted black. Available with four lights, five lights, six lights (like the antique), or eight lights. Height 15″; width 26½″; total length 54″ with 6 suspension links.
Five lights, electrified (shown) $110
Six lights, candles $95

K 12878 GUARDHOUSE LANTERN
Polished copper or copper finished black. Height 17⅜″; width 14¾″; projects 10½″.
One light, electrified $200

K 12879 WEST CARRIAGE GATE LANTERN
Polished copper or copper finished black. Height 22½″; width 11″; projects 9½″.
Two lights, electrified $230

K 12877 EAST CARRIAGE GATE LANTERN
Polished copper or copper finished black. Height 17¾″; width 11⅜″; projects 7″.
Two lights, electrified $200

*K 12877S SMALL EAST CARRIAGE GATE LANTERN
Size adaptation of K 12877 East Carriage Gate Lantern. Height 13″; width 6¾″; projects 4½″. Not shown.
Two lights, electrified $185

K 13161 WYTHE HOUSE KITCHEN SCONCE
Antique tin or tin painted black. Backplate height 8½″; width 2½″; projects 2¾″.
Electrified $10.50   Candle $5.00

K 13160 PALACE SAUCERBACK SCONCE
Antique tin or tin painted black. Height 10⅜″; diameter 9⅜″; projects 5½″.
Electrified $18.25   Candle $10.75

K 13159 PALACE CRIMPED-EDGE SCONCE
Antique tin or tin painted black. Height 13½″; diameter 11½″; projects 5¼″.
Electrified $20.75   Candle $13.25

K 13158 PALACE KITCHEN SCONCE
Antique tin or tin painted black. Height 12″; diameter 10″; projects 4½″.
Electrified $20.65   Candle $13.15

K 13162 SERVANTS' QUARTERS SCONCE
Antique tin or tin painted black. Height 10″; width 4½″; projects 4¾″.
Electrified $15.50   Candle $8.00

K 12578 RALEIGH TAVERN BAR CHANDELIER
Antique tin or tin painted black. Available with four lights, five lights, six lights, or eight lights (like the antique). Height 11½″; width 27½″; total length 50½″ with 6 suspension links.
Six arms, electrified (shown) $120
Eight arms, candles $105

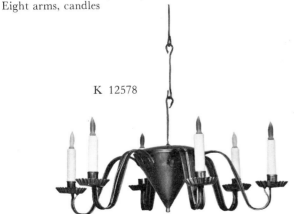

K 12578

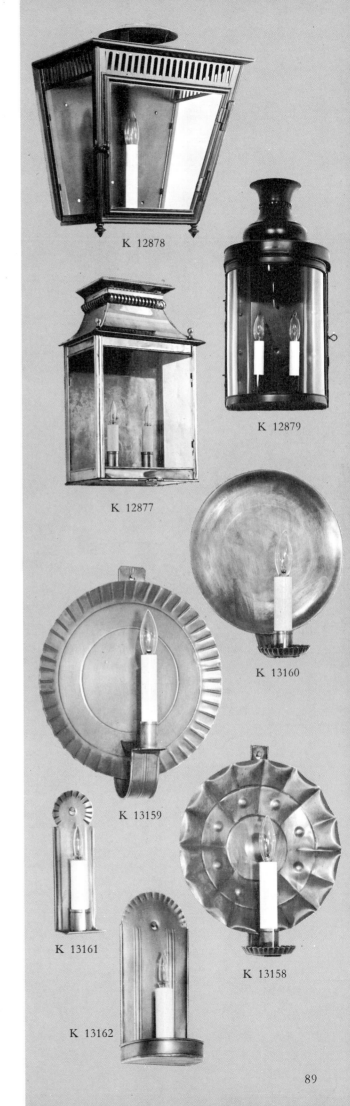

K 12878

K 12879

K 12877

K 13160

K 13159

K 13161

K 13158

K 13162

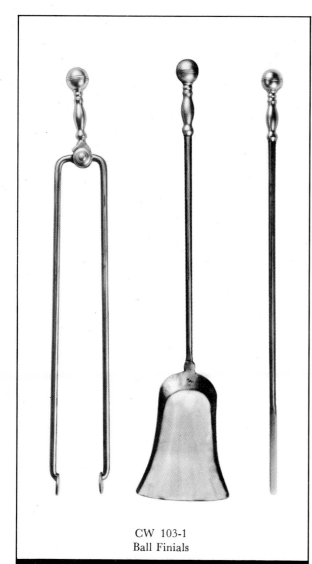

CW 103-1
Ball Finials

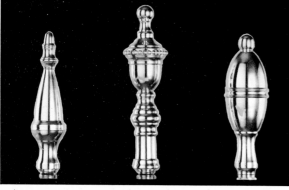

*CW 103-1A
Davis
Finials

*CW 103-1B
Claw-and-Ball
Finials

*CW 103-1C
Raleigh Tavern
Finials

Williamsburg

FIREPLACE ACCESSORIES
by The Harvin Company

TODAY, as in the most ancient times, man uses fire for his comfort and delight. The pleasures of the fireplace make it a natural focal point in any room, a source of light and heat and unequalled charm. The handsome accessories shown on these two pages will enhance the beauty of your fireplace, and dramatize this important area of your home.

CW 103-1 FIRETOOLS. These graceful brass and polished steel tools were copied from an antique set made in England in the last half of the eighteenth century. Like the originals, which are now in the Moody House, they have ball finials. They are also available with finials to match the CW 100-1 Claw-and-Ball Andirons, the CW 100-2 Raleigh Tavern Andirons, and the CW 100-4 Davis Andirons.

Average height 29″   Set with any finial design $98.00

CW 102-1 SERPENTINE FIREPLACE FENDER. A simple pierced pattern with a scalloped edge lends grace and dignity to this handsome brass fender. It was copied from an English antique, *circa* 1750-1775.

Height 6¾″; width 49¼″; depth 11⅝″ $179.00

*Adaptation

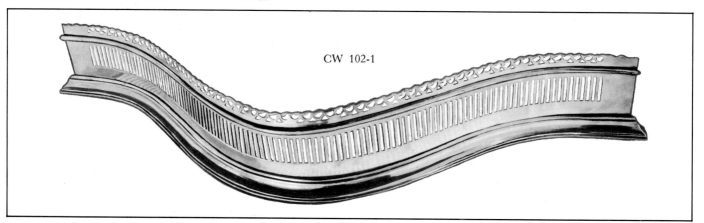

CW 102-1

CW 100-1

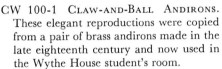

CW 100-4 Davis Andirons. The ball-and-steeple finials on these reproductions are unusually graceful. The brass andirons were copied from a pair of antiques in the Williamsburg collection. The antiques are marked "J. Davis, Boston", and were made about 1790.
Height 17″; depth 15½″ $90.00

CW 100-4

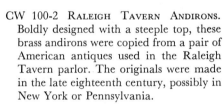

CW 100-2

CW 100-1 Claw-and-Ball Andirons. These elegant reproductions were copied from a pair of brass andirons made in the late eighteenth century and now used in the Wythe House student's room.
Height 24″; depth 22½″ $140.00

CW 100-2 Raleigh Tavern Andirons. Boldly designed with a steeple top, these brass andirons were copied from a pair of American antiques used in the Raleigh Tavern parlor. The originals were made in the late eighteenth century, possibly in New York or Pennsylvania.
Height 23½″; depth 22″ $120.00

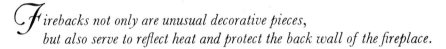

Firebacks not only are unusual decorative pieces, but also serve to reflect heat and protect the back wall of the fireplace.

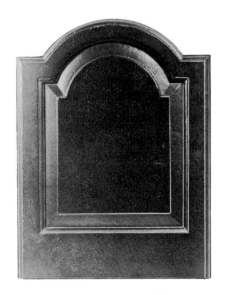

CW 101-3 Panel Fireback. This cast-iron fireback was copied from an antique used in the Governor's Palace. Fragments of a duplicate fireback were excavated at the site of the Palace; experts believe the two might have come from the same foundry and mold. The antique was made in the first half of the eighteenth century.
Height 24″; width 18½″ $40.00

CW 101-2 Virginia Fireback. The legend "Virginia 1737" decorates the face of this cast-iron fireback. The reproduction was copied from antique fragments excavated at the site of the Red Lion on Duke of Gloucester Street in Williamsburg.
Height 24″; width 20¾″ $40.00

CW 101-1 Charles Rex Fireback. The royal arms of King Charles I of England embellish this handsome cast-iron fireback. The reproduction was copied from an antique made in England in the second quarter of the seventeenth century, and now used in the Governor's Palace.
Height 23″; width 21″ $40.00

BRASS

CANDLESTICKS and ACCESSORIES

by

VIRGINIA METALCRAFTERS

VIRGINIA METALCRAFTERS of Waynesboro, Virginia, produces for Craft House the exciting collection of brass candlesticks and accessories shown on these pages. The graceful designs of antiques in the Williamsburg collection have been exactly copied by gifted craftsmen, using ancient techniques and superb skill of the hands.

The color of the eighteenth-century metal, whiter and brighter than modern brass, has been painstakingly reproduced. In addition, a special finish is applied to each piece of *Williamsburg* brass; this not only closes the pores of the metal so that it resists tarnish, but also polishes to a distinctive mellow patina.

CW 16-5 SQUARE BASE CANDLESTICK. The original of this fine reproduction may be seen in one of the committee rooms of the colonial Capitol. Its square base with ridged ball feet, a Queen Anne design of about 1720, is unusual.
Height 6¾″   Each $23.50   Pair $45.00

CW 16-12 MID-DRIP CANDLESTICK. The drip-pan on this handsome candlestick is both practical and graceful. This reproduction copies an antique, *circa* 1680, now used in the parlor of the George Wythe House.
Height 8½″   Each $26.00   Pair $50.00

CW 16-13 BRUSH-EVERARD CANDLESTICK. A seventeenth-century English candlestick now in the parlor of the Brush-Everard House was the model for this dramatic reproduction. Its bold curves, sausage turning, and flaring trumpet base are distinctive.
Height 8″   Each $28.50   Pair $55.00

CW 16-20 BALUSTER CANDLESTICK. Purity of line and perfect proportions distinguish this simple candlestick. Copied from an early eighteenth-century English antique now in the Raleigh Tavern, it is often used under the CW 9 Hurricane Shade (page 112).
Height 5¾″   Each $13.25   Pair $25.00

CW 16-12

CW 16-20

CW 16-13

CW 16-5

CW 16-33

CW 16-10

CW 16-63

CW 16-34

CW 16-35

CW 16-36

CW 16-73

CW 16-21

CW 16-10 SWIRL BASE CANDLESTICK. The elegant detail of this striking candlestick has been copied from an English antique made about 1750. The original is now in the Governor's Palace. Height 8¾"   Each $21.00   Pair $40.00

CW 16-21 CHAMBERSTICK. The original of this graceful chamberstick was made in the mid-eighteenth century and is now in the Raleigh Tavern. It is a pleasing table accessory.
Length, including handle 8½"; height 2½"   Each $15.50

CW 16-33 SPIKED CANDLESTICK. This massive and magnificent candlestick with wrought-iron spike was copied from a seventeenth-century English antique in the Capitol. It is dramatic alone or with the CW 10 Hurricane Shade (page 112). A white candle is included; for other candles, please see page 137.
Height exclusive of spike 7½"   Each $33.75   Pair $65.00

CW 16-34 TALL CANDLESTICK. More than a foot tall, this candlestick adds drama to any setting. It is a careful copy of an English antique in the Governor's Palace. The reproduction is also available as a two-light lamp without shade.
Height 12½"   Each $46.00   Each wired $64.40

CW 16-35 OCTAGONAL BASE CANDLESTICK. An eighteenth-century Dutch antique now in the Governor's Palace was copied to make this candlestick. It fits neatly under the CW 9 Hurricane Shade (page 112), and is charming in pairs on a small mantel. Height 7"   Each $18.35   Pair $35.00

CW 16-36 CANDLESTICK. A handsome antique, probably of French origin, has been copied to make this fine brass candlestick. The reproduction faithfully matches the graceful lines of the original which is now in the Governor's Palace.
Height 8¾"   Each $23.50   Pair $45.00

CW 16-63 CANDELABRA. A serpent's head decorates each branch of this elegant reproduction. Copied from an antique in the Governor's Palace, it has arms that move up or down and swivel to give a graceful entwined effect.
Height 16"   Each $66.45   Pair $130.00

CW 16-73 CANDLEHOLDER WITH SNUFFER. This delightful reproduction, copied from an old English piece, is excellent with colonial furnishings and charming in a contemporary room. Diameter 6"   Each $19.95

93

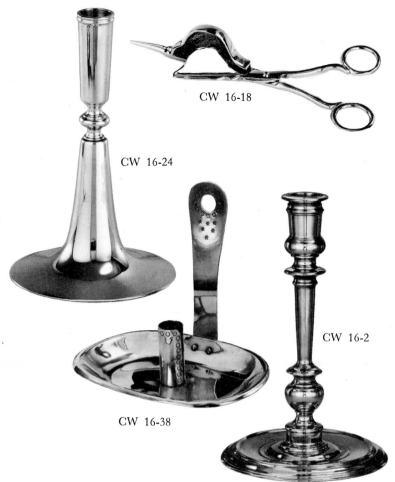

CW 16-18

CW 16-24

CW 16-38

CW 16-2

CW 16-2 ROUND BASE CANDLESTICK. The classic lines of this handsome candlestick add charm to any room. Used alone, in pairs, or with the CW 10 Hurricane Shade (page 112), it has a simple elegance that refreshes and pleases.
Height 8″   Each $18.50   Pair $35.00

CW 16-18 SCISSORS CANDLE SNUFFER. This delightful *Williamsburg* reproduction was copied from an English candle snuffer, made *circa* 1720-1735 and used now in the library of the Brush-Everard House.
Length 6¼″   Each $9.75

CW 16-24 TRUMPET BASE CANDLESTICK. Contemporary in spirit, this fine reproduction is a replica of a seventeenth-century English design. It has been copied from an antique in the George Wythe House.
Height 8¼″   Each $18.50   Pair $35.00

CW 16-38 CANDLEHOLDER. Copied from an eighteenth-century antique, this candleholder is charming on a wall or as an ash tray. Of special interest are six small stars decorating the graceful handle.
Height 6½″   Each $11.55

The CW 17-68 Door Knocker is seen on a handsome paneled door in Colonial Williamsburg.

DOOR KNOCKERS

CW 17-67 URN DOOR KNOCKER. This elegant reproduction is used on a number of Colonial Williamsburg's restored houses. The plain bar area is an appropriate place to engrave your name.
7¾″ x 4¼″ $13.95

CW 17-67

CW 17-68

CW 17-68 "S" DOOR KNOCKER. The classic design of this fine reproduction enhances any door, traditional or contemporary. Reproductions of this knocker are used on many doors in Colonial Williamsburg.
7¾″ x 2¾″ $20.45

BRASS RIM LOCKS *by FOLGER ADAM*

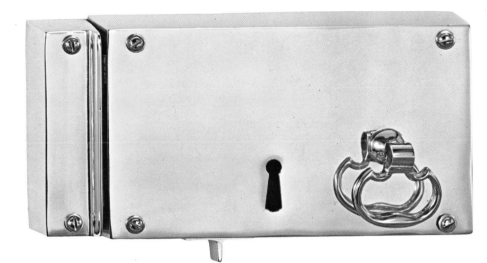

WILLIAMSBURG Brass Rim Lock Reproductions are manufactured by Folger Adam, for many years a pre-eminent manufacturer of fine hardware. These reproductions are careful copies of locks used in eighteenth-century Williamsburg and now seen again in Williamsburg's restored houses and Exhibition Buildings.

Locks are known to have been used in early civilizations, the oldest an Egyptian wood lock with a key so heavy only a grown man could carry it. Through the centuries locks were customarily elaborate and richly ornamental, until the late eighteenth century when the classic undecorated style was developed.

This handsome example, called a rim lock because the entire lock is exposed, is made of heavy brass, hand-filed and polished by expert craftsmen.

KEEPER   LEFT-HAND MEDIUM LOCK WITH DROP HANDLE

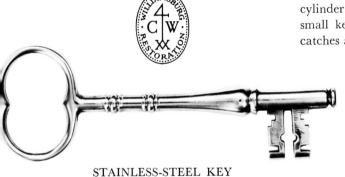

STAINLESS-STEEL KEY

THE *Williamsburg* Brass Rim Lock (above) is available with hand-turned brass knobs or drop handles (below), and includes a complete lock assembly with one large brass or stainless-steel key (left). For those who do not wish to carry a large colonial key, the lock is also made with a covered key plate (below), and with a modern cylinder lock unobtrusively fitted to the large lock and operated by a small key. Knob or drop handle sets for use with modern mortise catches are also available.

The locks are made in three different sizes to fit the scale of individual doors with right-hand or left-hand openings. The side of the door on which the keeper is placed determines whether the lock is right or left hand. Orders should specify lock size, whether left or right hand, the thickness of door, and preference for either brass or stainless steel key.

	With two knobs and colonial key	With one knob, one drop handle, and colonial key	With two drop handles and colonial key
#1 Large 10″ x 5½″ x 1⅜″	$124.50	$127.70	$131.75
#2 Medium 8″ x 4½″ x 1″	99.20	102.50	106.40
#3 Small 6¾″ x 3⅞″ x 1″	80.75	84.10	88.00

For additional price information, see Supplemental Price List.

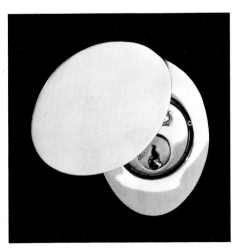

KEY PLATE AND CYLINDER LOCK

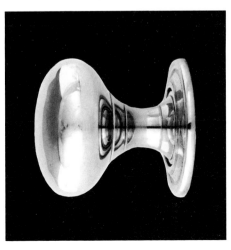

KNOB

DROP HANDLE

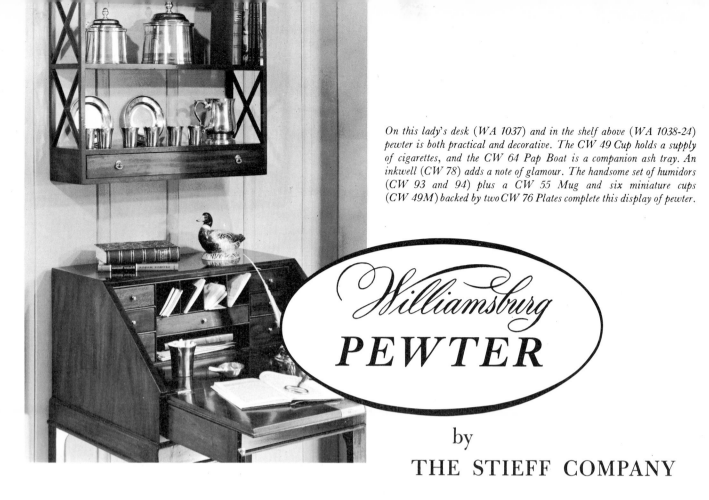

On this lady's desk (WA 1037) and in the shelf above (WA 1038-24) pewter is both practical and decorative. The CW 49 Cup holds a supply of cigarettes, and the CW 64 Pap Boat is a companion ash tray. An inkwell (CW 78) adds a note of glamour. The handsome set of humidors (CW 93 and 94) plus a CW 55 Mug and six miniature cups (CW 49M) backed by two CW 76 Plates complete this display of pewter.

Williamsburg PEWTER

by
THE STIEFF COMPANY

THE Stieff Company of Baltimore has reproduced for Craft House a group of fine pewter pieces, copied in detail from outstanding antiques now on display in Colonial Williamsburg's Exhibition Buildings. This *Williamsburg* pewter, made from an ancient formula of tin, copper, and antimony, has a characteristic mellow patina obtainable only in lead-free pewter. Its high luster can be maintained by thorough drying after each washing and by occasional use of a polish of high quality.

Pewter was the most widely used of all metals during the early days of the American colonies. Everything from dishes to sundials, from shoe buckles to barber bowls, was made of this useful metal. Before 1700, imports of pewter from England exceeded two million dollars in today's American currency and were in excess of 300 tons annually.

Not only the old formula, but also the old methods are used by Stieff's master craftsmen today in the production of *Williamsburg* pewter. Though these artisans no longer test the metal's temperature by poking it with a dry pine stick, the four important processes in pewter manufacture—casting, turning, burnishing, and polishing—require the same skill of the hands as they did so many years ago.

CW 80   CW 82   CW 81

*CW 80 TEAPOT. A smaller teapot now in the Raleigh Tavern inspired this distinctive adaptation. The antique was made in eighteenth-century London by Samuel Ellis.
Capacity 2¼ pints; height 8¼"
$66.75

CW 81 CREAMER. This graceful pear-shaped creamer is an exact reproduction of an English or American antique now in the Raleigh Tavern.
Height 3¼" $13.35

*CW 82 SUGAR. This sugar has been designed as a charming companion piece for the creamer described above.
Height 2¾" $13.35

*CW 83 LARGE CREAMER. A size adaptation of the CW 81.
Height 4¼" $15.75

*CW 84 LARGE SUGAR. A size adaptation of the CW 82.
Height 3½" $15.75

Set of CW 81 and CW 82 $25.50
Set of CW 80, CW 81, and CW 82 $90.50
Set of CW 83 and CW 84 $30.00
Set of CW 80, CW 83, and CW 84 $95.00

*Adaptation

CW 78

CW 93

CW 94

CW 64

CW 49

CW 49M

PEWTER was first made in a place and time as yet unknown to historians. The early Egyptians and Chaldeans are known to have used the metal, however, and the Chinese were proficient in its manufacture over a thousand years ago. Pewterware has been unearthed from the sites of Roman cities of the second century A.D. in England and France.

With the disintegration of the Roman Empire, European pewtermaking temporarily came to an end. After many hundreds of years pewter was again being crafted in eleventh-century England, but only for use in palaces and churches. As early as 1348 a pewterers' guild was formed in London, and at the time colonization of America began it had become a powerful trade organization. By the eighteenth century pewter had made its way into the life of aristocrat and servant alike.

Today this metal of ancient origin has once again come into fashion. The meticulous craftsmanship of each piece of *Williamsburg* pewter justifies the place of this lustrous metal in America's most distinguished homes.

CW 49 CUP. Copied from an eighteenth-century English beaker, this cup is equally suitable for a cocktail, a small bouquet, or cigarettes. On a desk it holds pencils and pens. A set, filled with frappé, makes a festive party.
Height 3″ — Each $5.45
Set of 6 $30.00

*CW 49M CUP. This two-ounce adaptation of the CW 49 Cup is an excellent jigger and a charming cigarette cup for a dining room table. Filled with a miniature flower arrangement, it is delightful on a bedside table.
Height 2″ — Each $3.05
Set of 6 $16.50

CW 64 PAP BOAT. The original of this unusual piece has the crowned X found on eighteenth-century English pewter of good quality. It is shown here used as a pipe holder. It is also a distinctive ash tray, particularly at each place at a dining table.
Length 4⅜″ — $5.05

CW 78 HELMET INKSTAND. The original, now in the secretary's office of the Governor's Palace, was made in England by Bush and Perkins *circa* 1770-1790. This fine reproduction adds charm to any desk and is also a unique container for flowers. A quill pen is included with each order.
Diameter 5″ — $23.35

*CW 93 HUMIDOR. This is a size adaptation of the larger CW 94 Humidor. It is a particularly charming desk accessory.
Over-all height 6″; diameter of base 5″ — $22.45

CW 94 HUMIDOR. Beautifully crafted, this handsome humidor is an exact copy of an English antique now used in the Apollo Room of the Raleigh Tavern. The antique was made by Anthony Jenner *circa* 1770-1780. This fine copy by Stieff holds cigars, tobacco, matches.
Over-all height 7¼″; diameter of base 6″ — $33.55

*Adaptation

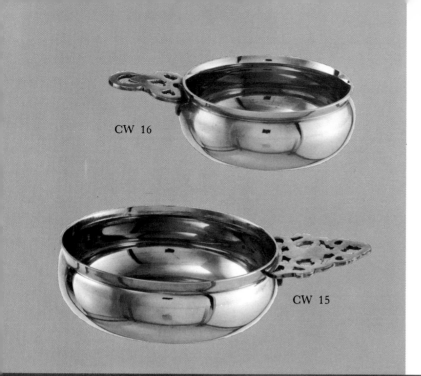

CW 55 TANKARD. This classic tankard is a familiar eighteenth-century design. A pair of these is a delightful wedding present; a set of six adds luster to any bar. Each tankard holds a pint.
Height 5" $18.35

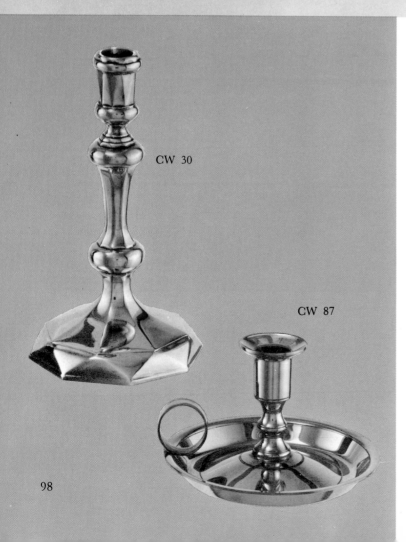

FOOTED BOWLS. Copied from an eighteenth-century English antique, these graceful bowls have many uses. The CW 10 is suitable for nuts, candy, sauces, or, as shown on page 99, for consommé. The larger sizes are excellent as serving bowls for vegetables or fruit; and the giant one is especially handsome filled with flowers.

	Diameter			Diameter	
CW 10	5½"	$10.35	*CW 6	9¼"	$28.45
*CW 5	7¼"	$17.35	*CW 7	11"	$46.30

CW 15 PORRINGER. The antique from which this porringer has been copied is on display in the Raleigh Tavern public dining room. It was made in England in the late eighteenth century. The reproduction is a fine small serving dish.
Diameter 4¼" $10.35

CW 16 PORRINGER. This bowl makes a charming christening present. For adults, it is a graceful ash tray or a serving dish for nuts, candy, or cocktail dip.
Diameter 3¼" $7.10

CW 30 CANDLESTICK. A pair of rare Queen Anne candlesticks was copied to make this unusual reproduction. Made in England, circa 1710-1720, the antiques may be seen in the Brush-Everard House. The unusual faceted base of the originals has been meticulously copied by Stieff's master craftsmen.
Height 7¼"   Each $23.25   Pair $45.00

CW 87 CHAMBERSTICK. An exact copy of an English antique in the Williamsburg collection, this charming pewter reproduction is a decorative table accessory. It is useful as a pipe rest, and a delightful way to provide soft candlelight.
Diameter 5¾"; height 3¼" $15.50

*Adaptation

In this table setting, sparkling pewter creates the mood for a delicious first course. CW 59 Place Plates, CW 10 Bowls, CW 76 Bread and Butters, CW 30 and 31 Candlesticks, CW 64 Pap Boats, the CW 96 and 97 Salt and Pepper, and the CW 99 Caster make a bright display of Williamsburg *pewter.*

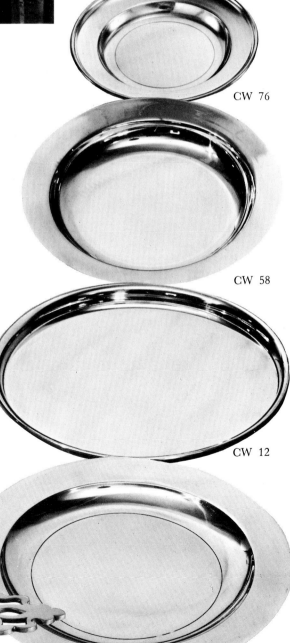

CW 76

CW 58

CW 12

CW 59

*CW 12 TRAY. The original from which this tray was adapted, was part of a miniature pewter service, probably of Continental origin. The adaptation is a distinctive serving tray.

Diameter 10½″ $15.75

CW 31 CANDLESTICK. The simplicity and grace of this distinctive candlestick were copied from an English antique now used in the Public Gaol in Williamsburg. The original dates from the late eighteenth century. The base of this candlestick is a narrow three inches.

Height 5½″   Each $17.25
     Pair $33.00

CW 58 SOUP PLATE. This plate is a reproduction of an eighteenth-century piece, probably of Continental origin. The handsome copy is shown filled with soup on page 100; it also makes a stunning ash tray.

Diameter 8¾″ $17.35

CW 59 PLACE PLATE. Suitable for serving sandwiches, cold meat, and hors d'oeuvres, this handsome plate has been copied from an antique in the Wythe House kitchen. It may be seen used as a place plate in the picture above and on page 100. The original was made in London about 1766-1777.

Diameter 11″ $17.60

CW 60 PORRINGER. A porringer made *circa* 1717-1738 by Edward Nash of London, and now in the Wythe House kitchen, is copied in detail in this reproduction. It makes a superb nut or candy bowl, flower container, or large ash tray. In the breakfast table setting on page 29 it is used to hold half a grapefruit.

Diameter 5¼″ $20.60

CW 76 PLATE. Copied from an eighteenth-century English antique now used in the Governor's Palace kitchen, this fine dish is an excellent small ash tray, bread-and-butter plate, or card tray.

Diameter 5¼″ $5.10

*Adaptation

CW 31   CW 60

CW 51

CW 3

CW 95

CW 85

Three CW 30 pewter candlesticks light this elegant table set with Williamsburg pewter. CW 58 Soup Plates fit neatly on CW 59 Plates, and CW 55 Mugs filled with draft beer invite even the most particular gourmet. A CW 3 Bowl, used for crackers, and pewter spoons (CW 53 and 56) complete this table of gleaming pewter. The tin sconces may be seen on page 89.

CW 9

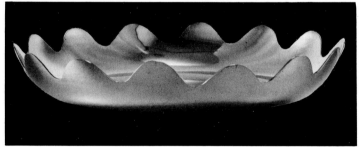

CW 54

CW 3 Bowl. An excellent bowl for fruit, vegetables, and flowers, this fine reproduction is a copy of a basin made by Thomas Badger of Boston *circa* 1790-1800.

Diameter 8″ $15.35

CW 9 Bowl. The original from which this fine bowl was copied has English hallmarks of the second half of the eighteenth century. Useful as a serving dish, it also fits the CW 5 mahogany basin stand, shown on page 23.

Diameter 10⅜″ $20.85

CW 51 Berry Spoon. This unusual spoon is an exact copy of an English antique dating back to the late sixteenth or early seventeenth century. It is particularly charming used with the CW 7 Lipped Finger Bowl (page 113).

Length 6¾″ $5.05

CW 54 Strawberry Dish. Copied from an Irish antique made *circa* 1690-1700 by William Bancks, this unusual scalloped bowl is stunning when piled high with colorful fruits.

Diameter 11½″ $20.60

CW 85 Sugar Scoop. This generous scoop is used effectively with the CW 10 Bowl (page 98) to serve nuts or condiments. It has been copied from an antique which bears the crowned X, symbol of English pewter of high quality.

Length 4⅞″ $3.05

*CW 95 Pitcher. A silver pitcher now used in the Wythe House dining room inspired this graceful pewter adaptation. The original was made in London in 1728-29 by Samuel Hitchcock. The fine copy holds 90 ounces.

Height 9½″ $66.75

*Adaptation

CW 92   CW 91

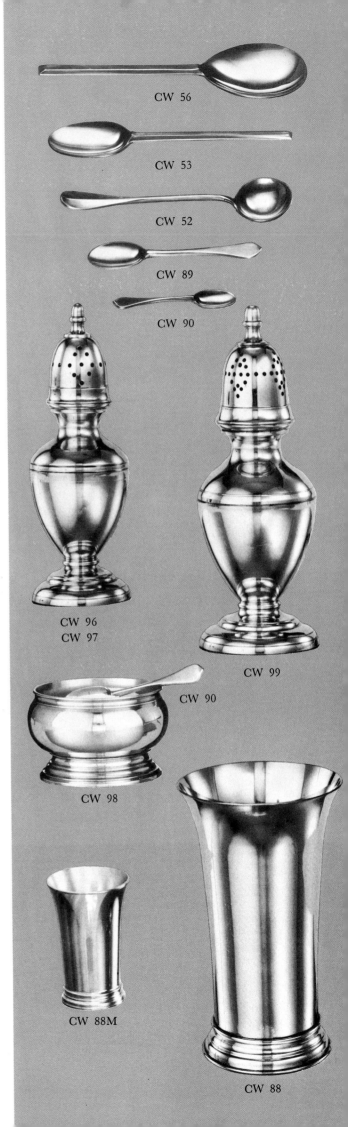

CW 56

CW 53

CW 52

CW 89

CW 90

CW 96
CW 97

CW 99

CW 90

CW 98

CW 88M

CW 88

CW 52 LADLE. This is an authentic copy of a type of ladle used in the late eighteenth century. Its shape and size are particularly suited for use with the CW 10 Bowl (page 100).
Length 5¾" $4.05

*CW 53 TEASPOON. This is a smaller version of the CW 56 Tablespoon. Copies are used in Chowning's Tavern in Williamsburg.
Length 6¼" $3.25

CW 56 TABLESPOON. A seventeenth-century spoon made in England was copied to make this sturdy pewter piece. Fine for serving, it is also a distinctive soup spoon and is shown in the table setting pictured on page 100.
Length 7" $3.80

CW 88 BEAKER. This handsome reproduction of an English antique is a classic vase for long-stemmed flowers. It has the unusually soft luster of all *Williamsburg* pewter.
Height 6¾" $17.35

*CW 88M CORDIAL CUP. A size adaptation of the CW 88 Beaker, this is a graceful and unusual cordial cup. It is also charming filled with a tiny bouquet.
Capacity 1 ounce; height 2¼"   Each $4.55
                                                       Set of 6 $24.75

*CW 89 COFFEE SPOON. Adapted from an English antique of the late seventeenth or early eighteenth century, this spoon is an unusually charming piece.
Length 4¼" $2.30

*CW 90 SALT SPOON. This tiny spoon is a miniature of the CW 89 Coffee Spoon. It is used ideally with the CW 98 Open Salt.
Length 3" $2.05

CW 91 CREAMER. The fanciful lip on this graceful creamer gives it a special charm. Its antique prototype was probably made in England in the last half of the eighteenth century.
Over-all height 4" $13.50

*CW 92 SUGAR. This adaptation was patterned after the CW 91 Creamer, and matches it in spirit and style.
Over-all height 3¾" $12.75
                                          Set CW 92 and CW 91 $24.75

*CW 97 PEPPER; CW 96 SALT. A pair of these, for salt and pepper, are a handsome addition to any dining table. They have been adapted from the larger CW 99 Caster. The CW 97 Pepper is equally attractive with the CW 98 Open Salt (see below).
Height 5⅛"   Each $15.35
                                                          Set $29.50

CW 98 OPEN SALT. Copied from an antique now used in the Governor's Palace kitchen, this piece has charming proportions. It is shown here with the CW 90 Salt Spoon, described above.
Diameter 2¾" $5.60
                                  Set CW 97, CW 98, and CW 90 $21.50

CW 99 CASTER. This handsome caster, or muffineer, is a copy of a late eighteenth-century English antique now used in the Raleigh Tavern. It is used today as it was in the eighteenth century to serve sugar and spices.
Height 7" $20.60

*Adaptation

STERLING SILVER REPRODUCTIONS
by STIEFF

WILLIAMSBURG SILVER REPRODUCTIONS combine the balance, strength, and satisfying proportions of the best eighteenth-century craftsmanship. Patterned after the silver used in a gracious, hospitable society, the hollow ware and flatware shown on the following pages have the direct simplicity and superb design characteristic of that elegant age. These handsome copies of colonial antiques, equally suitable in traditional and contemporary settings, increase in beauty with each day's use.

Even persons of modest means in colonial Virginia are known to have owned sterling silver. For the wealthy, sterling silver was a form of investment as well as a symbol of status and a necessary and appropriate part of table service. The graceful pistol-handled knives, three-tined forks, and rat-tailed spoons, and the handsome coffeepots, bowls, and pitchers now reproduced and available at Craft House, are as satisfying to own today as they were two hundred years ago.

The *Williamsburg* coffee service on the CW 8 Tea Table.

RT 29

RT 18

RT 15

RT 16

RT 19

RT 28

Sterling Silver
Tea and Coffee Service

RT 15 SUGAR BOWL. The simple elegance of this bowl was copied from a piece made 200 years ago by John Burt, a Boston silversmith. Capacity 10 ounces; height 2¾"; diameter 4" $45.60

   *RT 34 SMALL SUGAR BOWL (not shown). A small adaptation of the RT 15 Sugar Bowl. Capacity 5 ounces; height 2¼"; diameter 3¼" $30.60

RT 16 SUGAR BOWL COVER. The unusual shape of this cover is both practical and charming: it has its own foot and may be used separately as a small dish. It fits the RT 15 Sugar Bowl. Height 1¼"; diameter 4¼" $25.30

   *RT 35 SMALL SUGAR BOWL COVER (not shown). A smaller adaptation of the RT 16 Sugar Bowl Cover. It fits the RT 34 Small Sugar Bowl. Height 1"; diameter 3⅜" $24.80

*RT 18 CREAMER. This is a size adaptation of a creamer thought to have been made by John Allen, 1671-1760. Its shape echoes the soft curves of the RT 15 Sugar Bowl. Capacity 10 ounces; height 4½" $111.00

   RT 33 SMALL CREAMER (not shown). Smaller than the RT 18 Creamer, this is the companion to the RT 34 Small Sugar Bowl. Capacity 4 ounces; height 3½" $86.00

RT 19 TEAPOT. The boldly curved ebony handle on the *Williamsburg* teapot is in gracious balance to its melon-shaped body. Delicate hand engraving around the top is the only embellishment. The antique it copies was made by Jacob Hurd, a Boston silversmith. Capacity 1½ pints; height 6" $376.45

RT 28 BOWL. Copied from a bowl made by Philip Syng, 1676-1739, this fine reproduction serves beautifully as a waste bowl with the *Williamsburg* silver tea or coffee service. Capacity 18 ounces; height 2⅝"; diameter 5½" $53.10

RT 29 COFFEEPOT. The original of this magnificent coffeepot was made by Charles Le Roux, a New York silversmith. The straight spout and straight tapered sides are dramatized by the graceful curve of the ebony side handle. Capacity one quart; height 11" $555.00

*Adaptation

103

RT 23

RT 27

RT 66

RT 30

RT 32

RT 21

RT 67

Sterling Silver

RT 21 COMPOTE. This is an authentic copy of an old compote or salver made by Jacob Hurd of Boston *circa* 1702-1758. An old definition of salver says it was used in serving vessels of liquids ". . . to save the Carpit and Cloathes from drops." Today we use it for serving nuts, petits fours, and other delicacies.

    Height 3⅛"; diameter 8½" $101.25

    *RT 20 COMPOTE. A smaller adaptation of the RT 21 Compote (not shown).

      Height 2¼"; diameter 6⅝" $76.25

RT 23 FINGER BOWL. A copy of an unusual bowl made by Jacobus Van der Spiegel, a New York silversmith, this reproduction is an elegant finger bowl. With the RT 27 Tray, it is a charming dish for a child.

    Height 2"; diameter 3¾" $30.10

RT 26 SYRUP PITCHER. Paul Revere, Sr., the father of America's most celebrated silversmith, made the original from which this handsome pitcher was copied. Beautifully proportioned, it has the generous capacity of 10 ounces.

    Height 6¼" $146.25

RT 27 TRAY. Small and graceful, this tray may be used as a bread-and-butter plate, or to hold the RT 26 Syrup Pitcher or RT 23 Finger Bowl.

    Diameter 5" $24.30

RT 30 MUFFINEER. This caster was designed for sprinkling food with salt, spices, or sugar. Today it is a delightful way to serve powdered sugar. The antique bears the London hallmark of 1709-1710.

    Capacity 10 ounces; height 8⅞" $196.45

RT 32 INDIVIDUAL COFFEEPOT. A gracious touch on a breakfast tray or table, this charming *Williamsburg* coffeepot is particularly suitable for today's more leisurely living. The raffia-covered handle is heat-resistant.

    Capacity 10 ounces; height 5¼" $136.25

RT 66 SKEWER. This skewer is a reproduction of one made in York, England, by J. Hampton and J. Prince in 1780. A handsome letter opener, it is carefully hand-engraved with a bright-cut decoration.

    Length 9" $25.30

RT 67 BRANDY WARMER. Excellent for serving hot sauces, this fine reproduction was copied from an old English brandy warmer made by John Eckford in 1723.

    Capacity 8 ounces; height 2¼"; length including handle 6¾" $43.35

*Adaptation

Sterling Silver

RT 22 SAUCE OR GRAVY BOAT. John Burt, born in Boston in the seventeenth century, created the original of this sauce boat. A deeply curved handle balances the long graceful lip.
Capacity 10 ounces; over-all length 8″ $133.85

RT 24 CANDLESTICK. This classic candlestick was copied from one made by Timothy Bontecou, 1693-1784. The oval of the removable cup reflects the shape of the base.
Height 5½″ $61.15

RT 25 MUSTARD OR HORSE-RADISH POT. This glass-lined silver pot is a charming addition to any table. A row of beading decorates the straightforward design.
Height 2½″; diameter 2¼″ $101.00

RT 31 TRENCHER SALT. Copied from an antique made in London *circa* 1706-1707, this graceful open salt is a natural mate for the RT 36 Pepper Shaker below. It is glass-lined to guard the silver from corrosion.
Height 1¼″; diameter of base 2⅜″ $20.35

RT 36 PEPPER SHAKER. The antique from which this shaker was copied was made by Benjamin Burt, born in Boston in 1729. It may be used as a small muffineer for cinnamon or nutmeg, and is handsome with the RT 31 Trencher Salt.
Height 5¼″ $66.00

*RT 54 SALT SPOON. This is a smaller adaptation of the RT 12 Teaspoon.
Length 3″ $4.20

*Adaptation

Williamsburg PLATED SILVERWARE

FROM about 1742, when an English cutler discovered that silver and a base metal could be fused and worked like solid silver, plated ware has had a prominent place in the most distinguished homes. The Stieff Company has produced for the Reproductions Program two handsome items of plated ware, copied from antiques in Williamsburg, and made in the Stieff tradition of superb workmanship. These unusual pieces are superior to the best grade of superfine silver plate.

J 1 BOWL. A fine container for hors d'oeuvres or a centerpiece, this bowl is a silver plate adaptation of one made by Richard Gurney and Thomas Cook of London, *circa* 1746-1747. The original is in the Silversmith's Shop.
Height 3⅛″; diameter 7⅛″ $18.50

J 2 CANDLESTICK. The original from which this handsome candlestick was adapted may be seen today in the Silversmith's Shop in Williamsburg. The antique was made in London *circa* 1723-1724 by David Green.
Height 6¼″; width 3¾″   Each $20.25
   Pair $39.00

RT 61 Set of 6 steak knives boxed

RT 62

RT 69   RT 68

RT 51   RT 63

Williamsburg

REPRODUCTION FLATWARE

THE *Williamsburg* Queen Anne sterling silver pattern has been recognized for years as the most distinguished reproduction of eighteenth-century flatware. Copied from a design popular throughout most of the eighteenth century, the rat-tailed spoons, three-tined forks, and pistol-handled knives are cherished today as then for their graceful shapes and clean lines.

RT 1	Dinner Knife	10⅛″	$18.05
RT 2	Medium Knife	8½″	15.05
*†RT 3	Small Dinner Knife	9¼″	16.05
†RT 4	Dessert Spoon	6¾″	14.30
RT 5	Tablespoon	7⅞″	25.30
RT 6	Tablespoon (notched)	8⅜″	32.80
*†RT 7	Butter Spreader	6⅝″	10.25
RT 8	Coffee Spoon	4⅜″	5.95
†RT 9	Dinner Fork	7¾″	17.55
†RT 10	Medium Fork	6½″	13.25
*RT 11	Oyster Fork	5⅜″	9.20
*†RT 12	Teaspoon	5¾″	9.65
*RT 13	Iced-Tea Spoon	7″	13.75
*RT 14	Roast Carving Set	Knife 13⅜″ Fork 10½″	75.65
RT 51	Ladle	7″	15.30
*RT 54	Salt Spoon	3″	4.20
*RT 60	Cold Meat Fork	8½″	28.75
*RT 61	Steak Knife	8⅜″	16.75
		Set of 6, boxed	99.00
*RT 62	Steak Carving Set	Knife 10¼″ Fork 9¼″	45.60
*RT 63	Gravy Ladle	6⅜″	27.80
*RT 64	Fish Knife	7¼″	15.25
*RT 65	Salad Fork	6⅜″	13.25
*RT 68	Baby Spoon	4⅜″	7.70
*RT 69	Baby Fork	4½″	7.70
RT 70	Sugar Shell	See Supplement	11.20
†Six-Piece Place Setting			79.50

*Adaptation

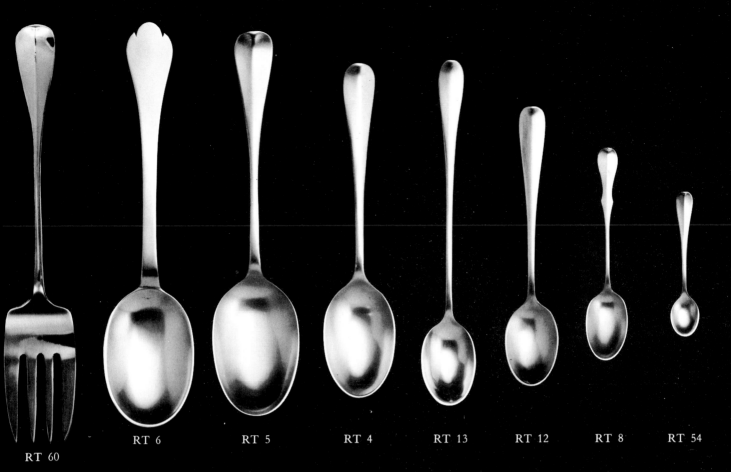

RT 60   RT 6   RT 5   RT 4   RT 13   RT 12   RT 8   RT 54

RT 14

RT 9   RT 65   RT 10   RT 11   RT 64   RT 61   RT 7   RT 2   RT 3   RT 1

*I*N this luxurious dining room the gracious hospitality of 200 years ago is re-created for today's living. Sparkling in the light of a warm fire, Williamsburg *reproduction sterling silver, glass, and dinnerware are complemented by the sheen of a polished mahogany table.* Williamsburg *table accessories are equally suited to the modern home, where their clean lines and simple curves appear refreshingly contemporary.*

WILLIAMSBURG GLASSWARE by Royal Leerdam

Williamsburg Glassware Reproductions are unequaled for beauty of design, purity of materials, and superb hand workmanship. Copied from fragments excavated in Williamsburg and from antiques in the Exhibition Buildings of Colonial Williamsburg, these exquisite reproductions are made of lead glass, a strong yet translucent glass with a unique power to diffuse light. Each piece has its individual characteristics, reflecting the skill of the artisan who produced it. Only the finest and most experienced craftsmen are entrusted with making these mouth-blown and hand-formed pieces, whose timeless designs are noted for their sophisticated simplicity.

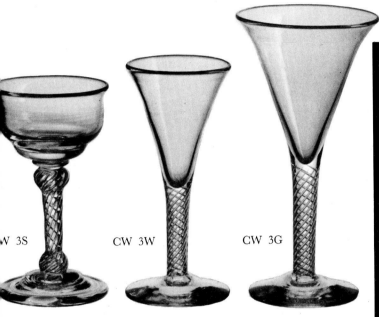

W 3S   CW 3W   CW 3G

AIR-TWIST

This spiral air-twist form was developed in about 1735 and was popular throughout the mid-years of the eighteenth century. Many fragments have been discovered in Williamsburg. In making the air-twist stemware, a wire is introduced into the molten stem to form a fistula. Several fistulas are successively formed and then combined and twisted into a graceful spiral by the use of wooden paddles and other special tools in the hands of a master craftsman.

	Height	Each	Half Dozen
CW 3G Goblet	7⅞"	$11.25	$64.75
CW 3W Wine Glass	6½"	11.25	64.75
CW 3S Sherbet/Champagne	5¾"	11.25	64.75

Williamsburg Stemware

CW 2G   CW 2W   CW 2S

TEARDROP

The teardrop in this intriguing pattern is formed by first introducing a wire into the molten stem. When a fistula forms, a wet stick is applied and the steam develops a "tear" which the craftsman chases up the stem to the desired spot. The *Williamsburg* teardrop sherbet or champagne glass is copied from an antique in the Williamsburg collection. There are also many fragments of teardrop stems in the Williamsburg archaeological collection.

	Height	Each	Half Dozen
CW 2G Goblet	7⅞"	$10.25	$58.75
CW 2W Wine Glass	6½"	10.25	58.75
CW 2S Sherbet/Champagne	5¾"	10.25	58.75

BALUSTER

Among the most common stem forms found during the excavations in Williamsburg was the inverted baluster with sloping domed foot, an English form of the first quarter of the eighteenth century. *Williamsburg* baluster stem glasses are handsome reproductions of this shape still popular today because its simplicity complements both contemporary and traditional settings.

	Height	Each	Half Dozen
CW 1G Goblet	7⅜"	$10.25	$58.75
CW 1W Wine Glass	5⅞"	10.25	58.75
CW 1S Sherbet/Champagne	5"	10.25	58.75

W 1G   CW 1W   CW 1S

Williamsburg Glassware for Entertaining

THE *Williamsburg* Glassware Reproductions shown on these two pages were designed in the hospitable days of two centuries ago. Their graceful and sophisticated shapes are equally suited to today's entertaining, where the finest in bar and dining glassware is once again in demand.

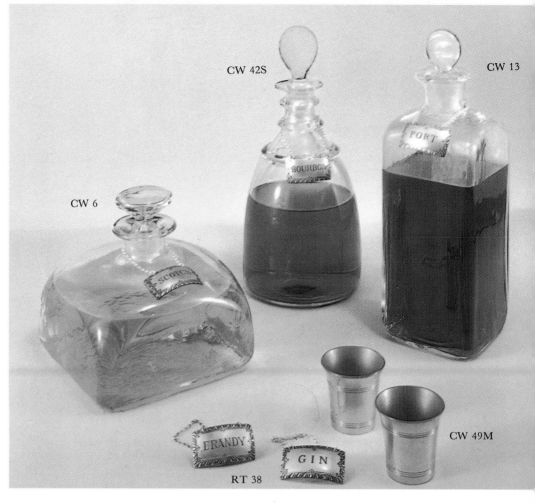

CW 6 SQUARE DECANTER. This charming decanter was copied from an antique designed for a cellarette. It is delightful alone, or used in pairs on the AP 120 Tray (see page 127).

Capacity 1½ quarts; height including stopper 6¼"; base 6" x 6"
$20.45

CW 13 TALL DECANTER. The pleasing shape of this decanter, popular in the eighteenth century, was copied from an antique once owned by a colonial resident of Williamsburg. It is also available in amethyst, emerald, sapphire, and amber.

Capacity 1⅓ quarts; height including stopper 11¼" $20.05

***CW 31S OLD-FASHIONED GLASS.** The CW 31L has been reduced in size to make this adaptation. It is available in amber, amethyst, sapphire, and emerald as well as crystal.

Height 3¼"   Each $5.60   Half Dozen $31.05

CW 31L DOUBLE OLD-FASHIONED GLASS. This handsome copy of a tumbler used during the eighteenth century is available in crystal as shown, and in amber, amethyst, sapphire, and emerald.

Height 4"   Each $6.25   Half Dozen $34.70

CW 34 TUMBLER. Copied exactly from an antique in the Williamsburg collection, this glass has a barrel shape which is particularly suited to informal settings. Available in crystal only.

Height 3⅝"   Not Available

***CW 42S DECANTER.** A very large decanter now in the Brush-Everard House has been reduced in size to make this graceful adaptation. It handles and pours with ease.

Capacity 1¼ quarts; height including stopper 11" $22.45

CW 49M PEWTER CUP. For information about these intriguing shot glasses or liqueur cups, please see page 97.

Each $3.05   Set of 6 $16.50

RT 38 LABELS. These sterling silver labels are described on page 135.

Each $5.95

CW 31L   CW 31S   CW 34

Shown above are color adaptations of three pieces of *Williamsburg* glass. Other selected pieces are also available in these brilliant colors—amethyst, emerald, and sapphire—in addition to the translucent crystal. Colors such as these were familiar to the colonial glass blower, as excavated fragments have shown.

*Adaptation

THE first glassmakers in America were "eight Dutchmen and Poles" who landed at Jamestown, Virginia, in 1608. They used techniques of glassmaking developed almost thirty-five centuries ago. Those same techniques are used today by the artisans at Royal Leerdam, one of the few glass manufacturers continuing the delicate art of off-hand glass blowing.

CW 5W

CW 5T

CW 5M

CW 5S

TAVERN GLASSES

This handsome set of glasses, inspired by a fragment in the Williamsburg archaeological collection, will lend a note of elegance to any party or table setting. The CW 5M is an exact reproduction; the other glasses are size adaptations. All are available in crystal, amber, amethyst, sapphire, and emerald.

	Height	Each	Half Dozen
*CW 5T Iced Tea	6⅛″	$5.50	$30.20
*CW 5W Water	5⅛″	5.35	29.55
CW 5M Old-Fashioned	4⅛″	4.85	26.55
*CW 5S Cocktail	2⅞″	3.10	15.75

*CW 38P WATER JUG

The simple lines of a graceful antique pitcher have been carefully reproduced in this fine adaptation. Etching which decorates the original has been omitted. The jug is available in crystal and in amber, amethyst, sapphire, and emerald. Capacity 1½ quarts; height 7⅞″ $17.45

CW 30

CW 14

CW 15

*CW 2P PILSENER GLASS

A fine adaptation of the authentic teardrop design, this glass is excellent for serving beer and ale. Its shape is pleasing to the hand, and its style is in the best eighteenth-century tradition. Available in crystal only. Height 7⅞″

Each $10.45
Half Dozen $58.75

*Adaptation

CW 30 BEAKER. An authentic copy of an antique in the Williamsburg collection, this beaker is of a type popular in the late eighteenth century. Designed as a drinking glass, it is also fine for flower arrangements. It is available in crystal, and in amber, amethyst, emerald, and sapphire. Height 5¾″.   Not available

CW 14 ETCHED FLIP GLASS. A cooling drink and a dainty bouquet of spring flowers are equally suited to this fluted crystal glass. The simple etched design exactly matches that of the original. Height 6⅜″   Not available

CW 15 PLAIN FLIP GLASS. This simple and handsome glass, available in crystal, and in amber, emerald, amethyst, and sapphire, is a stunning tall vase. Its shape is an exact reproduction of a fine English antique. Height 7½″ $10.45

Hurricane Shades

Four CW 16-34 cathedral candlesticks (page 93) are a handsome backdrop for the CW 10 Hurricane Shade filled with fruit.

Surrounded by a strawflower wreath, the CW 9 Shade is shown with the CW 16-35 Candlestick (page 93). Set $34.00

The CW 10 Hurricane Shade with a CW 16-33 Candlestick (page 93)
Set $52.50

ORIGINALLY used to protect candles from wind and drafts, hurricane shades are in fashion today for the same practical reason as well as for their decorative value. As shown above, a hurricane shade may be used on its side filled with colorful fruits, or upright surrounded by a wreath of flowers, to make charming holiday decorations or centerpieces.

These fine hurricane shades are size adaptations of an antique used in the upstairs hall of the Governor's Palace. They are available in crystal, amber, amethyst, sapphire, and emerald.

*CW 9 HURRICANE SHADE. Height 14″; inside diameter of base 4⅞″
Each $17.65   Pair $33.00

*CW 10 HURRICANE SHADE. Height 17¾″; inside diameter of base 5⅜″
Each $21.50   Pair $40.00

Emerald   Sapphire   Crystal   Amethyst

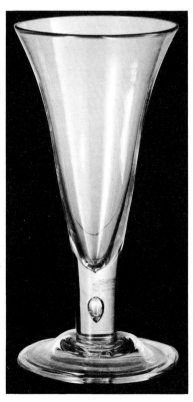

CW 36S PITCHER. This graceful reproduction (above) of a fine eighteenth-century original now in the Williamsburg collection may be used as a small creamer or for tiny flower arrangements. It is available in crystal, amber, amethyst, emerald, and sapphire. Height 3⅝″
$6.45

CW 36L PITCHER. Shown here in emerald, this pitcher is a larger adaptation of the 36S Pitcher. It is also available in crystal, amber, amethyst, and sapphire. Height 5″ $7.45

CW 2V TEARDROP VASE. A fine reproduction, this stunning vase is particularly suited to long-stemmed flowers. It is also available in a taller adaptation. Height 10″ $15.05

*CW 2VL TEARDROP VASE (not shown). A size adaptation of the CW 2V Vase. Height 11½″ $17.65

*Adaptation

CW 2V

To produce the fine glassware for the reproductions program, Royal Leerdam craftsmen blow a "gather" of molten glass into a bubble on a blowpipe, then hold it on a pontil rod, swiftly turning the bubble of glass and manipulating it into the shape desired. When the shape satisfies the craftsman, the glass is snapped from the rod and cooled slowly in an annealing oven.

CW 7 LIPPED FINGER BOWL

Our forefathers used lipped finger bowls to rinse their wine glass between wine courses. Today they are used charmingly as finger bowls, and for ice, nuts, dessert, or flowers. This reproduction was copied from an antique in the Williamsburg collection, and is available in amber as well as crystal and the three jewel-like colors shown above. The pewter spoon in the crystal bowl is the CW 51 and may be seen on page 100.

Height 4¼"; diameter at top 4½" $6.35

CW 12 WINE BOTTLE →

This graceful bottle was copied from one in the Raleigh Tavern. It is a fine vase for ivy, and makes a distinctive decanter or carafe. It is available in amethyst, amber, emerald, and sapphire.

Height 8⅞" $8.25

CW 41 RUMMER

An unusual fish bowl and a magnificent container for a large bouquet of flowers and leaves, this fine reproduction was copied from an antique now in the Brush-Everard House. The original once belonged to the Stratton family of the Eastern Shore of Virginia.

Capacity 1 gallon; height 9½"; diameter across top 8⅜"

Not available

CW 40 WINE BOTTLE

This reproduction bottle bears a bottle button with the inscription: "Jno. Greenhow Wmsbg. 1770." It was copied from a bottle excavated at the site of the John Greenhow House and Store. It is available in amethyst, emerald, sapphire, and amber.

Capacity 26 ounces; height 8" $13.25

Williamsburg

Queen's Ware by Wedgwood

I N 1759 Josiah Wedgwood, a skilled and successful potter, founded a firm of potters in Burslem, England. Today Josiah Wedgwood and Sons is known the world over for the quality and distinction of its ceramic ware.

The handsome reproductions, commemoratives, and fancies that appear on these pages and on the two which follow are the work of this distinguished firm. Each item in this unusual collection is made of Queen's Ware, an invention of Josiah Wedgwood, who said in 1767, "The demand for this . . . Queen's Ware . . . still increases. It is really amazing how rapidly the use of it has spread almost over the whole globe, and how universally it is liked." Originally called cream ware by its inventor, it was soon to bear the name Queen's Ware at the command of Queen Charlotte of England, whose admiration for Wedgwood's work was further expressed when she made him "Potter to Her Majesty."

The tradition of excellence established by Josiah Wedgwood is carried on by his descendants, who work today with the same high standards of design, skill, and integrity he set two hundred years ago.

For a complete price list of all shapes, please see the Supplemental Price List.

HUSK

This classic pattern on Queen's Shape was copied from an antique plate in the Williamsburg collection, from drawings in old Wedgwood pattern books, and from eighteenth-century molds still in the possession of the Wedgwood Company. Fragments of this pattern have also been excavated in Williamsburg. Like the original, this excellent reproduction is cream-colored with the design in soft shades of mulberry. It is interesting to note that the same firm which was making this dinnerware for sale to Williamsburg colonists is once again producing it for sale in Williamsburg.

Five-piece place setting $17.25
Matching linen place mats and napkins are $6.00 for a set of two mats and two napkins.

The green Shell Edge pattern makes an inviting breakfast table.

All patterns now in guaranteed open stock

SHELL EDGE

Copied in detail from archaeological fragments, this fine dinnerware is a faithful reproduction of a pattern popular in Williamsburg in the latter part of the eighteenth century. Its simple design and unobtrusive decoration make it particularly suitable for today's distinctive tables. Hand-painted, it is available decorated with a blue edge (above) or a green edge (left). Fragments of both colors were unearthed in Williamsburg.

Five-piece place setting $14.70

Williamsburg Dinnerware

By WEDGWOOD

THREE famous Wedgwood shapes designed in the eighteenth century by Josiah Wedgwood are represented in five charming *Williamsburg* Dinnerware patterns by Wedgwood. They are Traditional, Shell, and Queen's Shape.

Carefully hand-crafted, these shapes have been skillfully painted by hand or decorated by color transfer printing in sophisticated patterns of soft colors.

Dinnerware is priced by the place setting. For a complete price list of all shapes, please see the Supplemental Price List.

Potpourri

POTPOURRI

Named for Queen Charlotte, Wedgwood's Queen's Shape dinnerware has been made continuously since 1765. In this delightful commemorative, it is imaginatively decorated in a rich fruit and flower pattern taken from an antique fabric. For information about the fabric, which has been reproduced, please see page 65.

Five-piece place setting $14.70

WILDFLOWERS

The *Williamsburg* Wildflowers fabric inspired this delicate pattern, which is skillfully transfer-printed on Wedgwood's Shell Shape dinnerware. Classic and serene, this commemorative pattern has an unusual charm. The fabric is illustrated on page 70.

Five-piece place setting $17.25

Wildflowers

AVIARY

Birds were a popular eighteenth-century decorative motif. This striking design on Wedgwood's Traditional Shape was taken from an eighteenth-century handkerchief printed from a copperplate engraving. The design of this commemorative pattern is in soft sepia tones.

Five-piece place setting $17.25

Linen place mats and napkins to match these commemorative patterns are $6.00 for a set of two mats and two napkins.

Aviary

Queen's Shape

Shell Shape

Traditional Shape

115

THE QUARTER

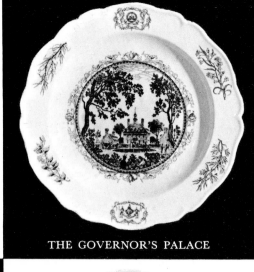

THE GOVERNOR'S PALACE

THE MAGAZINE

THE CAPITOL

THE GEORGE WYTHE HOUSE

THE PUBLIC GAOL

THE WREN BUILDING

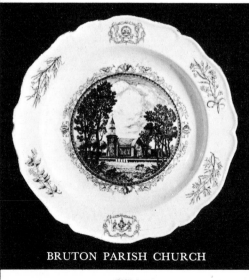

BRUTON PARISH CHURCH

ARCHIBALD BLAIR'S STOREHOUSE

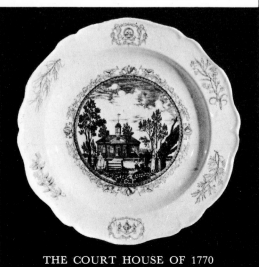

THE COURT HOUSE OF 1770

THE RALEIGH TAVERN

THE ST. GEORGE TUCKER HOUSE

Commemorative Plates and Fancies

By WEDGWOOD

THIS group of Queen's Ware fancies and the set of twelve *Williamsburg* Commemorative Plates have been popular *Williamsburg* gifts for many years.

THE COMMEMORATIVE PLATES shown at the left follow in the long-established American tradition of commemorating historic events and places on fine ceramic ware. Twelve Williamsburg scenes are represented with a rare combination of reality and fantasy which makes these plates outstanding among modern commemoratives. The distinguished American artist Samuel Chamberlain created the imaginative designs.

For the borders, sprays of Virginia flowers were copied from the eighteenth-century copperplate found in Oxford's Bodleian Library that also provided the only known contemporary views of portions of eighteenth-century Williamsburg. The cartouches at the top and bottom of the border enclose the seal of Colonial Williamsburg and the arms of Virginia. On the back of each plate is Mr. Chamberlain's signature, as well as a description of the center scene.

Centuries-old methods are used in transferring the designs from hand-engraved copperplates to the Queen's Ware body, and firing them under the glaze. In this process the strong composition and delicate color values of the sepia engravings are faithfully reproduced on each plate.

Twelve different center designs, as shown at the left, are available. The plates, 10 inches in diameter, may be used for dinner or service plates.

Sets of three, $12.75 each set

SET A: The Quarter, Governor's Palace, Magazine.

SET B: The Capitol, George Wythe House, Public Gaol.

SET C: The Wren Building, Bruton Parish Church, Archibald Blair's Storehouse.

SET D: The Courthouse of 1770, Raleigh Tavern, St. George Tucker House.

Complete set of 12, $44.00

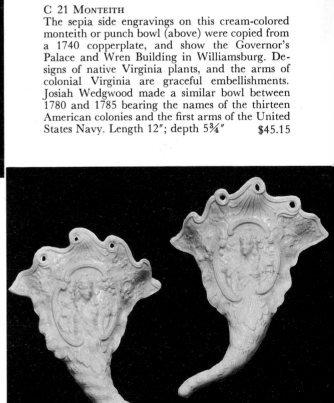

C 21 MONTEITH

The sepia side engravings on this cream-colored monteith or punch bowl (above) were copied from a 1740 copperplate, and show the Governor's Palace and Wren Building in Williamsburg. Designs of native Virginia plants, and the arms of colonial Virginia are graceful embellishments. Josiah Wedgwood made a similar bowl between 1780 and 1785 bearing the names of the thirteen American colonies and the first arms of the United States Navy. Length 12″; depth 5¾″ $45.15

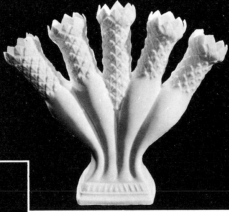

C 4 POSY HOLDER →
Reproduced from an English Staffordshire "finger vase" made about 1770, the famous *Williamsburg* Posy Holder (right) is a delight to the flower arranger. Fanciful arrangements can be made in it with only a few flowers. Height 7¾″
Each $19.65
Pair $37.90

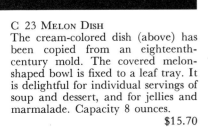

C 23 MELON DISH

The cream-colored dish (above) has been copied from an eighteenth-century mold. The covered melon-shaped bowl is fixed to a leaf tray. It is delightful for individual servings of soup and dessert, and for jellies and marmalade. Capacity 8 ounces.
$15.70

*C 22 CORNUCOPIA →
Effective as wall ornaments with or without flowers, these wall pockets (right) have been adapted in size from a pair belonging to Colonial Williamsburg. Filled with grapes and ivy leaves they are an attractive table centerpiece and are particularly appealing with dried flowers (page 123). The originals are Staffordshire salt glaze, made in England *circa* 1760. Height 10″
Each $20.70
Pair $39.90

*Adaptation

Williamsburg DELFT *by Oud Delft of Nijmegen*

D ELFTWARE, the colonial housewife's common pottery, today is treasured in the finest homes for its unusual charm and style. For the discriminating collector and decorator, Messrs. Oud Delft of Nijmegen, Holland, have copied for Craft House a selection of rare delft antiques in the Colonial Williamsburg collection. The grace and rich colors of the fine originals are now available in these authentic *Williamsburg* Delft Reproductions.

So exact are these copies that Williamsburg Restoration, Incorporated, has asked the manufacturer to impress an identifying date into each piece so that none may be mistaken for an antique.

C 5

C 5

C 5 JARDINIERE. This square polychrome brick is adaptable to a variety of flower arrangements. It is a faithful copy of a Bristol delft jardiniere, made *circa* 1730. Height 4″
Each $15.45
Pair $29.75

C 50 MIXING JUG. This charming blue and white pitcher is decorated with figures suggesting Elijah and St. Francis of Assisi. The gay striped spout is fed from a hole at the bottom, an excellent ice-catcher. The original was made in Southwark, England, about 1640.
Height 5⅛″; capacity 18 oz. $13.00

C 10

C 50

C 51

C 32 JAR. The original of this delicate vase, made in Liverpool in the mid-eighteenth century, can be seen in the George Wythe House. In the summer months it is charming filled with sweet peas or small daisies; in the winter, with small dried flowers. Height 5½″ $7.95

C 10 DELFT PLATE. A delightful ash tray or wall decoration, this authentic reproduction was copied from an eighteenth-century English plate found at the site of the Chiswell-Bucktrout House. The design, in two shades of blue, shows the Chinese influence. Diameter 10¼″ $15.55

C 51 PORRINGER. Copied from a Lambeth delft antique in Colonial Williamsburg's Apothecary Shop, this pleasing replica makes an unusual consommé bowl, and is equally suitable for serving nuts and candies. The antique was made *circa* 1720-30. Height 2⅛″; over-all diameter 5½″
$8.00

C 29

WILLIAMSBURG BRICKS

Round or square or oblong, the brick was popular in the eighteenth century as an inkwell or flower vase. Delft bricks—including some of these reproductions—are used as flower containers in the Exhibition Buildings of Colonial Williamsburg.

C 29 BLUE BRICK. The Wincanton Mimosa design is hand-painted in the familiar delft colors on this fine replica of an English antique. The original dates from the second quarter of the eighteenth century. Height 3½"; length 5¾"

Each $12.95
Pair $24.50

C 27 POLYCHROME BRICK.
A reproduction of a Bristol delft piece of the mid-eighteenth century, this container is subtly painted in soft blue and purple. Filled with plants, two of these bricks make excellent book ends. Height 3½"; length 6"

Each $15.45
Pair $29.75

C 26

C 26

C 26 CHINESE BRICK. Gaily decorated in soft delft colors, these bricks are delightful with small flowers or greens. They have been copied from a piece of Bristol delft made *circa* 1740. Height 2½"; length 4½"

Each $7.95
Pair $14.50

C 48 PITCHER. Two Chinese figures, a distant town, and a graceful tree decorate this handsome pear-shaped pitcher. It is a copy of an English antique, *circa* 1760. Over-all height 9¼"; capacity 2 quarts $26.00

*C 31 CREAM JUG. Hand-painted in brilliant polychrome, the pitcher shown here was inspired by a smaller jug made in Liverpool about 1760. The original is in the Raleigh Tavern public dining room. Height 4½"
$8.45

*Adaptation

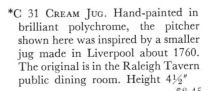

119

WILLIAMSBURG DELFT REPRODUCTIONS, imported for Craft House by Foreign Advisory Service Corporation, are made with essentially the same techniques as were used two hundred years ago. Each piece is first lightly fired, then dipped in tin-enamel, and finally hand-painted by a skilled artist. After another firing, a lead glaze is applied for brilliance, then one last firing completes the meticulous process.

*C 38 CANDLESTICK. This engaging candlestick has been adapted from the top section of a very rare, mid-eighteenth-century Lambeth delft food warmer. Like the antique, this copy has been meticulously hand-painted in a crisp blue design. Height 2½″   Each $6.45
                      Pair $11.95

C 45 VASE. A flawless reproduction of a magnificent Bristol delft antique, made about 1760, this blue and white vase is a dramatic accent in any room. It is stunning filled with large flowers or leaves, and makes a superb planter (as shown on page 41). Height 9¾″ $31.00

C 30 VASE. The classic urn shape of this Bristol delft piece designed between 1710 and 1720 is ornamented with a stylized decorative motif. Filled with fresh flowers, it is a bright note in any room. Height 6″ $9.95

*C 33 PITCHER. Multicolored flowers decorate this gay adaptation of a salt-glazed antique made about 1750-60. Filled with milk or waffle batter, it is a charming and useful addition to the breakfast table. Height 6¼″; capacity 1¼ quarts $15.05

*Adaptation

C 30

C 41 POLYCHROME SAUCER. This tiny saucer is ornamented with an intriguing hand-painted design. It was copied from an antique excavated in Williamsburg. Two or four make a fine set of individual ash trays. Diameter 4½″
$5.25

C 47 SHELL TRAY. Decorated with a Chinese scene, this small dish was copied from an old piece made in Liverpool *circa* 1750. Originally used for sweetmeats, it is a charming ash tray for the dining table. Width 3¾″
$3.30

C 55 SWEETMEAT TRAY. The stylized flowers on the border, and the blue and white house in the center are typical of English delft motifs of about 1740. Side length 4¾″
$4.30

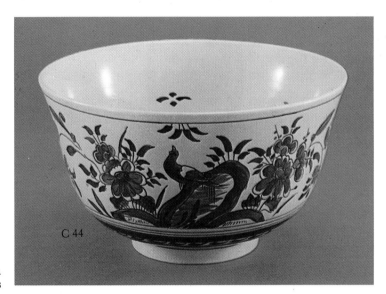

C 44 PUNCH BOWL. Filled with punch, or used as a centerpiece full of flowers or fruit, this generous bowl is a handsome addition to any table. Its simple shape is enhanced by a graceful design of birds, flowers, and leaves. The original was excavated in fragments from the site of the Coke-Garrett House in Williamsburg and laboriously restored. Height 5⅝″; diameter 10½″ $26.60

C 39 VASE. This vase, decorated with a Chinese figure and an Oriental landscape, is copied from a piece of Lambeth delft, *circa* 1750. Height 6¾″ $13.15

C 49 VASE. An English antique, made about 1700 and now in Williamsburg's Apothecary Shop, was copied to make this fine vase. Also suitable as a lamp base, it is painted with three scenes of figures and landscapes. Height 10¼″; diameter of top 4½″ $26.75

C 52 OVAL DISH. Painted with a design of birds, rocks, and flowers, this unusual reproduction is an excellent small planter or a distinctive nut dish. The antique, made about 1690, was probably used for potted meat. Height 3¼″; length 7″ $13.15

C 53 CASTER. Useful for sugar or cinnamon, and delightful for bath powder, this caster is a copy of a piece of Dutch delft made in the eighteenth century. Height 6⅜″; over-all diameter of base 3″ $10.25

C 54 MUG. This bell-shaped mug is a copy of an antique made in Lambeth about 1760. A set of eight or twelve with the C 44 Punch Bowl makes an unusual party table. Height 5″; capacity 12 ounces $10.15

C 40 ROUND BRICK. Copied from a piece of Lambeth delft made about 1700, this charming brick (shown at left and below) is decorated with intriguing ornamental symbols. Without the removable top it is a pleasing small serving bowl, and with the top it is delightful filled with flowers. Diameter 6″ $13.15

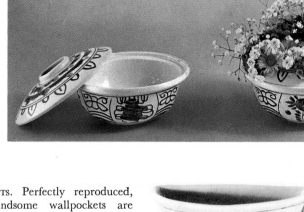

WALLPOCKETS. Perfectly reproduced, these handsome wallpockets are copied from antiques made in Lambeth about 1750. They were designed to be used in pairs with plants or flowers, but may be used singly for an unusual wall decoration. At left, dried flowers are shown arranged in one of these graceful reproductions.

C 36 Chinese Boy. Height 8″   Each $15.65

C 37 Chinese Girl. Height 8″   Each $15.65
                                 Pair $27.80

C 36   C 37

C 25 APOTHECARY JAR. This handsome jar was copied in detail from one of a pair of late-eighteenth-century English antiques now in the Apothecary Shop in Williamsburg. Height 7¾″
                                        $22.40

C 28 INKWELL. A fine copy of an antique in the Williamsburg collection, this inkwell is not only a desk accessory but also a delight filled with a small nosegay. The original is a piece of Continental tin-enameled earthenware. Height 1¾″; width 4¾″ $18.95

Dried Flowers

A large box of dried flowers was used to make this arrangement in the C 4 Posy Holder (see page 117).

DURING the winter months, bouquets of dried flowers may be seen in the Exhibition Buildings of Colonial Williamsburg. Called "everlastings" in colonial days, these flowers lend warmth and excitement to cold sunless days when fresh flowers are scarce.

The use of dried flowers in Williamsburg's colonial buildings has its precedent in the eighteenth century when mass bouquets of bright everlastings were widely used in harmony with the elaborate furnishings, spacious rooms, and forthright colors of the period.

Today's flower arranger will take equal delight in creating arrangements with the dried flowers offered at Craft House. Adaptable to both contemporary and traditional designs,

the selection in each box includes a wide variety of leaves and bright blossoms such as cockscomb, strawflowers, magnolia, celosia, babies'-breath, yellow yarrow, and larkspur.

To make a massed arrangement with these dried flowers fill a container with sand. Against a background of leaves, arrange tall spikes of material, then come forward with filler material. Next add strawflowers, celosia, and other round, weighty flowers and work them into an S curve or crescent design. Small pieces of spike material should then be arranged at the base of the arrangement to give depth to the design.

S 84

S 84 DRIED FLOWERS. Large box. Complete instructions come with this generous bouquet of dried flowers. The selection is available in the following predominant colors: red, pink, gold, pastel, or mixed. $23.75

S 84½ DRIED FLOWERS. Medium box. This selection contains approximately two-thirds the amount of flowers in the large box, and is available in the same choice of predominant colors. $18.00

FIGURES and CHARACTER JUGS of WILLIAMSBURG

By ROYAL DOULTON

THE eighteenth-century fondness for decorative ceramics has inspired this group of delightful figures and character jugs by Royal Doulton. The character jugs are the direct and charming descendants of the eighteenth-century "Toby Jug," that fanciful and humorous figure jug cherished by collectors for two centuries. And the group of exquisite figures has countless precedents from two hundred years ago, when, for example, a catalogue of the Chelsea Porcelain Manufactory offered among other items "new and beautiful Groupes of Figures," including figures of fishermen, a fisherwoman, a cobbler and his wife, a cook, and a woodcutter. Today Royal Doulton perpetuates these old traditions with the figures and character jugs shown here.

GAOLER

GUARDSMAN

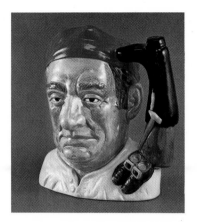

BOOTMAKER

BLACKSMITH

APOTHECARY

NIGHT WATCHMAN

Character Jugs of Williamsburg

CREATED as decorative pieces as well as fine collectors' items, these character jugs are vigorous characterizations of seven Williamsburg craftsmen who today wear the dress and ply the trades of their eighteenth-century predecessors. The larger size is an unusual container for flowers and leaves, and the two smaller versions hold cigarettes, matches, or pencils. All of these commemorative jugs are hand-painted.

Available in three sizes:

Large	Height 7″	$14.70
Small	Height 4″	$7.40
Miniature	Height 2½″	$4.45

GUNSMITH

Figures of Williamsburg

DOULTON and Company, Incorporated, has created a group of delightful figures modeled on men and women who lived in Williamsburg two hundred years ago and whose counterparts may be seen in Williamsburg today. These exquisite bone china figures, 6 to 8 inches high, are modeled and painted by hand by Doulton's master craftsmen. In their perfection, these authentic Royal Doulton figures embody all the traditions, the research, the skill, and the artistry of years of English craftsmanship.

RD 1
STANDING HOSTESS
Height 7½″
$43.10

RD 2
GENTLEMAN
Height 6¼″
$48.60

RD 8
CHILD
Height 5½″
$28.00

RD 5
SEATED LADY
Height 6″
$48.60

RD 4
SILVERSMITH
Height 6¼″
$55.60

RD 6
WIGMAKER
Height 7½″
$55.60

RD 7
BLACKSMITH
Height 7″
$55.60

RD 3
COOK
Height 6″
$48.60

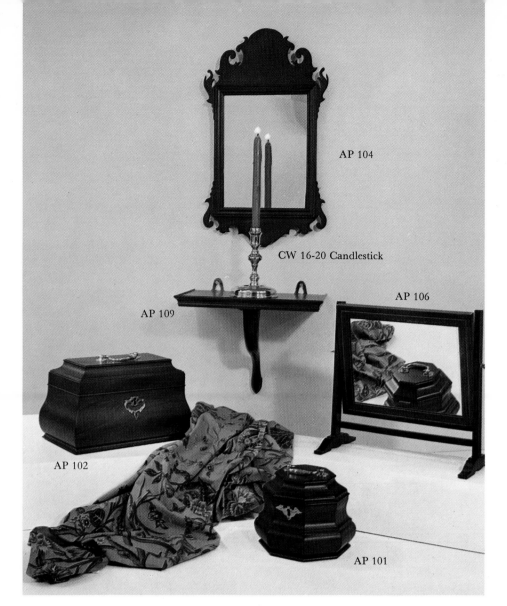

AP 104

CW 16-20 Candlestick

AP 106

AP 109

AP 102

AP 101

AP 104 CHIPPENDALE MIRROR. The frame of this fine mirror is copied in detail from an antique, hand-cut in about 1770. The crisp Chippendale design of scrolls and curves is distinctive on this delicate piece.

Over-all height 19½″; width 9½″
$54.80

AP 106 SHAVING MIRROR. This charming mirror, available in cherry or mahogany, is inlaid with satinwood. Delightful on dressing table or chest, it adjusts to many positions.

Height 11½″; width 11″ $31.40

AP 109 WALL BRACKET. A fine copy of an antique made about 1760, this wall bracket is excellent for holding a small clock, a candlestick, or several small ornaments.

Height 9″; width 12½″; depth 8″
$36.30
Set of AP 104, CW 16-20, and AP 109
$97.50

Williamsburg
WOODEN ACCESSORIES

EACH wooden accessory in the Reproductions Program is handmade by local craftsmen. Copied in exquisite detail from eighteenth-century antiques belonging to Colonial Williamsburg, these fine accessories are meticulously cut, assembled, and finished by hand in the ancient tradition of superb craftsmanship.

AP 101 OCTAGONAL TEA CADDY. Made of more than 25 hand-assembled parts, this mahogany container has a foil lining and polished brass hardware. It is copied from an English piece made about 1760 and is suitable for jewelry, cards, or tobacco.

Height 4¾″; diameter 6¼″ $35.60

*AP 102 OBLONG TEA CADDY. This mahogany caddy has three compartments with removable partitions. The original, now in the Governor's Palace, was made in England about 1760. It is a handsome container for cigarettes or cards. Also available velvet lined and fitted as a jewel box.

Height 6″; length 10″; depth 6″ $50.85
AP 102-J JEWEL BOX $58.50

*Adaptation in solid mahogany. Original is veneer.

Above, the AP 102 is shown with a whole carton of king-size cigarettes and the AP 101 with a treasured jewelry collection.

Four pewter liqueur cups (CW 88M Cup, page 101) are shown here on the AP 105 Tray.

Set of tray and 4 cups $28.00

AP 105 Small Tray. Particularly suited to serving liqueurs, this fine mahogany tray is a meticulous copy of an antique on display in the Colonial Williamsburg Information Center. 6½″ x 9½″ $11.60

The AP 120 Tray holds two square decanters, shown here with sterling silver labels. See the CW 6 Decanter on page 110 and a choice of RT 38 Labels on page 134.

Set $84.00

CW 16-80 Hurricane Candleholder. The pedestal of this unusual candleholder is made of mahogany and supports a 12-inch mouth-blown hurricane globe. It is a handsome accessory for any table, indoors or out.
Over-all height 16¼″ $43.50

AP 120 Gallery Serving Tray. This unusual mahogany tray, copied from an antique now used in the Governor's Palace, has a pierced and mitered rim and carved hand holes. Alcohol and heat resistant, it is an excellent cocktail or tea tray. Two are handsome "in-and-out" baskets on an executive's desk.
9½″ x 16½″ $36.15

WYTHE HOUSE CLOCK

The Wythe House Clock is an authentic reproduction of a late-eighteenth-century English clock on exhibit in the George Wythe House in Williamsburg. Its hand-rubbed solid mahogany cabinet is enriched with an inlaid design of hollywood. The feet, sash, and top handle are of solid brass. Both the key-wound and electric models have modern mechanisms of the finest quality, assuring long and accurate service. Height (with handle extended) 10½″; width 7½″; depth 4″; diameter of dial 3⅞″

A Wythe House Clock on an AP 109 Wall Bracket (page 126).

*Electric Non-Striking	$162
*8-Day Non-Striking	187
*8-Day Striking	257

POTTERY by Williamsburg Pottery

THESE delightful reproductions have been faithfully copied from fragments excavated in Williamsburg and Jamestown, and from antiques in the Williamsburg collection. Handmade by local craftsmen, they are characteristic of earthenware used in the area during colonial days. Included are examples of dotware, scratchware, marbleware, combware, and salt glaze.

M 5   DB 5   M 18   M 13   M 8   M 9   DP 2   M 7   M 25   M 1   M 3

DP 2 PITCHER AND DB 5 BOWL. The design of these dotware pieces is an early form of slip decoration. This charming pair is yellow with dark brown dots.

*DP 2 PITCHER. Height 3½″	$3.75
*DB 5 BOWL. Height 3″	3.60
Set of one DP 2 and one DB 5	6.60

†M 1 BEER MUG. The design of this yellow and brown mug dates back to the early settlement at Jamestown, Virginia. Height 5″; capacity 16 ounces   Each $3.75   Set of 6 $18.85

M 3 MEDIUM BOWL. A set of these yellow and brown bowls is delightful for serving individual casseroles and soups. The sgraffito or scratchware decoration is charming. Ovenproof.

†M 3 MEDIUM BOWL. Diameter 6½″	$4.75
†M 2 SMALL BOWL (not shown). Diameter 4¾″	3.75
†M 4 LARGE BOWL (not shown). Diameter 7¾″	7.05

M 5 LARGE TRENCHER. This large yellow and brown serving dish is copied from an antique in the Raleigh Tavern. Its comb decoration is a typical eighteenth-century slipware motif. Length 16¾″ $16.75

Also available but not shown are two size adaptations. All are ovenproof.

M 6 SMALL TRENCHER. Length 8¼″	$3.75
M 14 MINIATURE TRENCHER. Length 4″	$2.60

*Adaptation
†Not a reproduction

M 7 SLIPWARE PITCHER. Copied from fragments found at the site of the Semple House, this pitcher is yellow with streaks of brown. The fragments date from the early eighteenth century. Height 6″; capacity 24 ounces $5.85

M 8 MEDIUM JUG AND M 9 LARGE JUG. Copied from two antiques now used in the Raleigh Tavern, these gray stoneware jugs are salt glaze with cobalt blue decorations. The originals were made in Germany for the English market.

M 8 MEDIUM JUG. Height 6″; capacity 18 ounces	$5.85
M 9 LARGE JUG. Height 8″; capacity 36 ounces	$7.85

M 13 JAMESTOWN CANDLESTICK. The original of this unusual slipware candlestick was found in Jamestown. It is copied in yellow glaze with brown decoration. Height 6″ $4.75

M 18 DOTWARE CANDLESTICK. This charming chamberstick was re-created from fragments excavated at the site of Anthony Hay's cabinetmaking shop. It is yellow with brown dots. Height 2½″; diameter 4″ $2.60

M 25 PIE PLATE. Copied from fragments unearthed in Williamsburg, this marbled slipware plate is an excellent ash tray, as well as an unusual pie plate or serving dish. The rich browns and yellows are particularly pleasing. Diameter 10¼″ $5.95

Also available but not shown are two size adaptations.

*M 26 MEDIUM PLATE. Diameter 7½″	$3.25
*M 27 SMALL PLATE. Diameter 5½″	$2.60

M 10   M 12

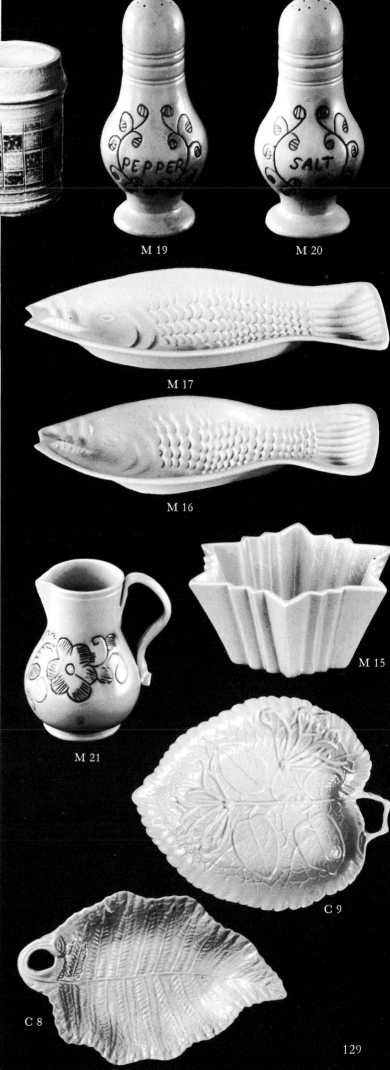

M 19   M 20

M 17

M 16

M 21   M 15

C 9

C 8

SALT GLAZE STONEWARE

STONEWARE, a hard pottery impervious to liquids and acids, takes on an unusual textured glaze (very like an orange peel) when common salt is thrown into the white-hot kiln. This "salt glaze" technique was invented by German potters of the fifteenth century, and was refined by the eighteenth-century English potter John Astbury, who is generally thought to have perfected the use of calcined flint to produce a white salt glaze stoneware.

The techniques developed by these early artisans are used today in the hand-crafting of *Williamsburg* Salt Glaze Stoneware. Approximately 25 hand operations are required in the creation of every piece of this distinctive pottery.

SALT GLAZE MUGS

These gray salt glaze mugs with cobalt blue decorations were inspired by fragments from the Williamsburg archaeological collection.

†M 10 MEDIUM MUG. Height 5″; capacity 12 ounces
　　　　　Each $2.75　Set of 6 $12.85

†M 11 LARGE MUG. Height 5½″; capacity 22 ounces
　　　　　Each $4.85　Set of 6 $25.30

†M 12 CHILD'S MUG. Height 3¾″; capacity 8 ounces
　　　　　Each $2.75　Set of 6 $12.55

†M 11S MUG. Also available but not shown is a size adaptation of the M 11 which is used in Chowning's Tavern.
　　Height 6¼″; capacity 15 ounces
　　　　　Each $3.85　Set of 6 $19.55

M 15 STAR MOLD. A delightful salt glaze mold for fancy gelatins, this small star is a copy of an antique mold, and is ovenproof. Height 1½″; diameter 3½″　　$2.35

M 16 AND M 17 FISH MOLDS. The M 16 Mold is a copy of an antique; the M 17 is a slightly larger adaptation. Both are made of purified white salt glaze, and are ovenproof. They make excellent pin trays, ash trays, and individual hors d'oeuvre plates.
　　　M 16 FISH MOLD. Length 5⅞″　　$2.25
　　　*M 17 FISH MOLD. Length 8⅛″　　$3.60

*M 19 AND M 20 PEPPER AND SALT SHAKERS. A Staffordshire salt glaze shaker now used in the Wythe House dining room was copied to make these charming adaptations. The original was decorated in enamel about 1760; the adaptation is decorated in a scratch blue design. Height 5″
　　　　　　　　　　　　　　　Set $5.50

M 21 PITCHER. Copied from an English antique of about 1760, this charming pitcher has a scratch decoration in blue. In this kind of ware, the design is scratched into the soft clay and blue cobalt is painted in the scratches.
Height 3½″　　$4.60

C 8 FERN TRAY AND C 9 HONEYSUCKLE TRAYS. These graceful dishes have been copied from antique sweetmeat trays made in Staffordshire, England, about 1760. Like the antiques, these reproductions are footed.
　　　C 8 FERN TRAY. Length 6″　　$3.10
　　　C 9 HONEYSUCKLE TRAY. Length 6½″　　$4.60

*Adaptation
†Not a reproduction

PRINTS by The Dietz Press

COPIED from valuable old works, the prints shown on this page are unusually effective decorations for today's fine homes. They include a pair of colored cartoons, a print from the famed Bodleian Plate, and an early map of Virginia. The Dietz Press has reproduced the originals with meticulous care. For other Dietz prints, see page 84.

P 2 Four O'Clock in Town

P 3 Four O'Clock in the Country

ROWLANDSON PRINTS

This pair of delightful cartoons was copied from antiques hanging in the bar of the Raleigh Tavern. The originals were designed and etched in 1788 by Thomas Rowlandson. Colored in muted tones of blue, yellow, and beige the reproductions are amusing and attactive decorations.

Unframed, 19″ x 16″ including margins	Each	$3.30
	Pair	$6.00
Framed in black and gold molding (shown), 18½″ x 15¼″		
	Each	$16.75
	Pair	$31.50

P 4 BODLEIAN PLATE. This is a copy of a print from a copperplate of about 1740, preserved by the Bodleian Library, Oxford, and given by them to Mr. John D. Rockefeller, Jr. It shows the then existing public buildings of Williamsburg and native Virginia flora and fauna. It provided important evidence for the restoration of Williamsburg. Black and white.

17¼″ x 13¾″ including margins   Unframed $2.30
Framed in black and gold molding, 18½″ x 15″ $16.00

P 6 MAP OF VIRGINIA. The original of this print was a map published in Amsterdam in 1640 and hanging now in the Raleigh Tavern. It is one of the earliest maps of the Virginia colony, and shows the location of Indian tribes and villages. Black and white.

18″ x 15¾″ including margins   Unframed $2.30
Framed in black and gold molding, 19¼″ x 17″ $16.00

P 7 HISTORICAL MAP. This hand-colored map of colonial Tidewater Virginia shows Jamestown, Williamsburg, and Yorktown with historic events in the area from 1585 to 1781. Included are the settlement at Jamestown, Bacon's Rebellion, the surrender at Yorktown, and other memorable events in early American history. The map was executed by Robert Ball.

Unframed, 24¾" x 18" including
margins $4.80
Framed in natural pine (shown),
26" x 19¾" $17.55

MAPS and PRINTS

The unusual collection of maps and prints shown on these two pages has been carefully designed to add charm and interest to any home. Just as prints were widely used in the eighteenth century, so today decorators recognize that fine prints add distinction wherever they are used.

WILLIAMSBURG MILITARY PRINTS

THESE four colorful military prints were executed in France by the well-known military artist Eugene Leliepvre. The uniforms and equipment of the soldiers are shown in meticulous detail, and each print is hand-tinted. The four regiments illustrated were important in pre-Revolutionary and Revolutionary Virginia history; a detailed explanation and history of the regiments is included with the prints.

Unframed 9¾" x 12¾"

Framed in ½" gold frame with red mat or
¾" walnut frame with green mat

Each $2.65
Set of 4 $8.70
Each $14.40
Set of 4 $50.30

1. Officer—Virginia Regiment and Virginia Militia, French & Indian War

2. Officer—44th Regiment of Foot, 1755

3. 48th Regiment of Foot, 1755

4. British Marines, 1775

CW 10-10

C-W 10-9

CW 10-11

CW 10-14

CW 10-11

CW 10-17

CW 10-17

CW 10-14

CW 10-10

C-W 10-9

A potpourri of imaginative gifts is offered in this exciting array of *Williamsburg* souvenirs. Reproductions, commemorative items reminiscent of Williamsburg, and a selection of unusual toys are included in this charming collection of gifts and souvenirs. Browse through the next 10 pages and choose delightful gifts for any occasion and for any age.

TRIVETS

IN colonial days trivets were used chiefly as stands for hot foods brought into the house from an outdoor kitchen. Today trivets are used for decoration, as well as to protect fine wood from hot dishes, water pitchers, potted plants, and flower vases. Williamsburg trivets are commemorative items based on eighteenth-century royal monograms, royal arms, and cyphers.

CW 10-10 Queen Anne Trivet. Queen Anne, who reigned in England from 1702 until her death in 1714, is remembered in this handsome trivet. It is a copy of her monogram, and is composed of the initials "AR", representing the Latin "Anna Regina." Available in brass or iron. 9″ x 10½″.

Brass $14.05   Iron $5.05

CW 10-9 King George Trivet. This trivet is a copy of the monogram of George II, King of England from 1727 to 1760. Available in brass or iron. 4″ x 5″.

Brass $5.25   Iron $1.50

CW 10-11 William and Mary Trivet. The monogram is that of William and Mary, who reigned jointly as sovereigns of Great Britain from 1689 until Mary's death in 1694. Available in brass or iron. 6″ x 8″.

Brass $9.95   Iron $3.45

CW 10-14 Colonial Williamsburg Trivet. This embellished cypher in low relief is composed of the initials "CW". It is an interpretation of a cypher form that would have been used by wealthy colonials to mark their important possessions. Available in brass, iron, verdigris, or white bronze. Diameter 6″.

Brass $6.95   White Bronze $7.95
Iron $2.95   Verdigris $3.95

CW 10-17 King's Arms Trivet. Available in brass or iron, this trivet copies the coat of arms on the sign of the famous King's Arms Tavern in Williamsburg. 5½″ x 6″.

Brass $8.95   Iron $2.95

S 66½ POTPOURRI PACKETS   S 66 POTPOURRI
                                          Bottle

S 137 HAND-WOVEN TOWELS   S 105 HERB TOWELS

The mixture of dried herbs, flowers, and spices in these colorful packages gives a delightful fragrance to linen closet, blanket chest, or chest of drawers. The envelopes are illustrated from a group of eighteenth-century mezzotints in the Williamsburg collection, showing the four seasons of the year.

S 66 Bottle	4¼ ounces Each	$4.25
S 66½ Packet	6½″ x 5″ Each	1.35
	Set of 4	5.20

S 137 These hand towels, of 50% linen and 50% cotton, are hand-woven in the traditional "M's and O's" weave, and are white with a choice of red, blue, brown, or yellow decoration. 14½″ x 20½″
Set of 3 in any color combination $6.25

S 105 A drawing of the John Blair Kitchen and herb garden decorates this set of three linen towels. They are printed in red, blue, or yellow, with green backgrounds.
Set of 3 (one of each color) $3.85

← S 132 SAMPLER KIT
The Governor's Palace in Williamsburg is the subject of this charming sampler. The kit contains a stamped sampler on 100% Belgian linen, embroidery thread, and complete instructions. Frame not included.
Cut size 14″ x 16″
$1.70

S 132

CREWEL KITS

The piquant designs of these *Williamsburg* Crewel Kits were adapted from an antique American bedspread made about 1765 and now in the Williamsburg collection. Each kit contains a silk-screen design, hand-printed on finest Belgian linen; 100% wool imported from England; a professional English crewel needle; and complete step-by-step instructions. The colors included are dull marine blue, bright rose pink, honeysuckle yellow, heraldic gold, and peacock blue. 12″ x 13″

S 140 Bird at Top	$3.65
S 141 Bird at Bottom	$3.65

S 142 SAMPLER KIT

Copied from a sampler worked in 1760 by 11-year-old Mary Starker, this reproduction duplicates the gay colors and charming design of the original in the Williamsburg collection. A picture of a dog chasing a stag at the bottom of the sampler has given this delightful piece the title "The Chase." Mary Starker's name, place of birth "Newbury, New England," and a pious ejaculation "Goodness and Mercy Ever follow [t]hose who shape there Conduct by Gods Holy Laws" have been deleted from this version of the sampler so that each person may stitch her own name into the sampler.

The kit contains a stamped sampler, on 100% Belgian linen, embroidery thread, and complete instructions. 16½″ x 24½″ cut size $7.15

The black frame illustrated is also available.
$10.50

133

CW 24-80

CW 18-62

CW 7-45

RT 53

CW 3-66

CW 3-35

CW 24-71

S 120S

CW 7-21

RT 38

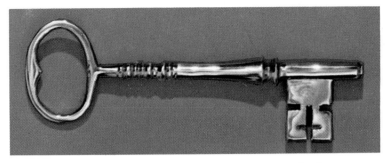

CW 6-44 KEY. A copy in brass of one of the keys to the Governor's Palace, this excellent paperweight is a highly decorative gift. Length 8″ $6.75

Williamsburg LEAF TRAYS. These leaf trays are based on trees and plants which were indigenous to eighteenth-century Williamsburg. The trays make exceptionally handsome and practical ash trays.

CW 3-66 ENGLISH PRIMROSE LEAF TRAY.
Brass; length 4½″ $4.70

CW 3-35 AMERICAN HOLLY LEAF TRAY.
Brass; length 4″ Pair $6.20

CW 7-21 HOLLY LEAF PAPER CLIP. This unusual desk accessory was inspired by an American holly leaf like those found in Williamsburg. Made of polished brass, it will keep papers in order and add charm to any desk. Length 4½″ $5.20

*CW 7-45 RANDOLPH PAPER CLIP. The plate of this intriguing piece is an exact copy in brass of an old harness ornament bearing the Randolph family crest. The base and spring have been added to make it an ideal paper clip or paperweight. 4½″ x 3″ $6.70

*CW 18-62 PRESSING IRON. A replica of an original on exhibit in the Williamsburg Archaeological Museum, this iron is useful as a book end or doorstop. Length 5″ $4.75

*CW 24-71 LION AND UNICORN PIN. This handsome pin in polished brass was copied from a keyhole escutcheon excavated at the Governor's Palace. 1¾″ x 2¼″ $5.15

*CW 24-80 CORKSCREW. Made of brass and steel, this useful tool is an authentic copy of an eighteenth-century English corkscrew. Length 5″ $7.75

*RT 38 DECANTER LABELS. Reproduced from eighteenth-century labels with antique lettering, these sterling silver labels are available for Rye, Scotch, Bourbon, Port, Sherry, Brandy, Rum, Gin, and Vodka. Label 1¾″ x 1″; chain 6″ $5.95

RT 53 KING'S ARMS PIN. This sterling silver pin is based on the coat of arms on the sign of the King's Arms Tavern. The arms are those of George I, George II, and George III. 2″ x 2″.
RT 53 PIN $6.70

CAPITOL MACE PIN. This mace pin was designed after the mace used in the colonial Capitol in Williamsburg. Length 3¼″
S 120G GOLD WASH $2.65
S 120S SILVER WASH $2.15

*Reproduction

RT 50 LAPEL PIN. This sterling silver pin was inspired by a large silver and gold cup, date marked 1649, in the Williamsburg collection. The pin holds water to keep small flowers fresh. 1½″ x 2¼″ $16.70

CW 3-27 PAPER MULBERRY LEAF TRAY. The design of this ample tray is based on the leaf of the romantic paper mulberry trees which line Blair Street in Williamsburg. Brass; length 5½″ $5.20

S48 *Williamsburg* MACE PIN. This miniature of the mace of the city of Williamsburg is available in a choice of silver or gold wash. The original mace bears the mark of a London silversmith of 1749. Length 3¾″ $1.40

RT 55 SPOON PIN. This sterling silver pin is a miniature copy of the rat-tailed spoon design popular in the eighteenth century. Length 3″ $5.20

S 79

S 80

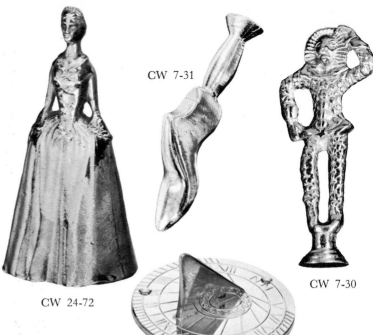
CW 7-31

CW 7-30

S 116

S 117

CW 24-72

CW 43

S 139-3

S 139-4

S 139-1

S 139-2

CW 24-20 GINGERBREAD MAN MOLD. An oak mold in the Raleigh Tavern Bakery inspired this delightful metal adaptation. Slightly smaller than the original, it is unusually decorative as well as excellent for molding cookies. 5¾″ x 11¼″ $9.00

Williamsburg SCENIC TILES. These sepia tiles protect the table from hot dishes and are decorative wall ornaments. Four of Colonial Williamsburg's most important buildings are illustrated. 6″ x 6″   Each $1.45   Set of 4 $4.85
S 79 Capitol   S 116 Bruton Parish Church
S 80 Governor's Palace   S 117 Raleigh Tavern

CW 24-72 *Williamsburg* HOSTESS BELL. Colonial Williamsburg's hostesses, dressed in the fashion of 1760-65, inspired this delightful bell. Available in polished brass or white bronze. Height 5″   Brass $8.10
White Bronze $10.60

*CW 7-30 HARLEQUIN PIPE TAMPER. This fanciful pipe tamper was copied from an early-eighteenth-century "tobacco stopper." It is made of brass. Length 2¾″ $2.15

*CW 7-31 SLIPPER PIPE TAMPER. Made in the shape of a lady's slipper, this brass pipe tamper is a replica of an antique. Such tampers were first devised by seventeenth-century craftsmen. Length 2¾″ $2.15

*CW 43 SUNDIAL. An eighteenth-century American craftsman made the original of this pewter piece. It is an unusual paperweight or ornament, and may also be attached to a window ledge or garden table to serve its original purpose. Diameter 3″ $3.45

Williamsburg MILITARY TILES. Four eighteenth-century military units are commemorated on these charming tiles. The illustrations are done in the style of eighteenth-century cartoons, and have the same subjects and colors as the military prints shown on page 131. 6″ x 6″
Each $2.95
Set of 4 $9.85
S 139-1 Virginia Militia   S 139-3 48th Regiment
S 139-2 44th Regiment   S 139-4 British Marines

*Reproduction

CW 24-45 HESSIAN SOLDIER COOKIE MOLD. Copied from a wooden antique in the Raleigh Tavern Bakery, this aluminum mold is slightly smaller than the original. It is charming on the kitchen wall, and is a fine cookie mold. 5¾″ x 11″ $9.00

S 119   S 69   R 4

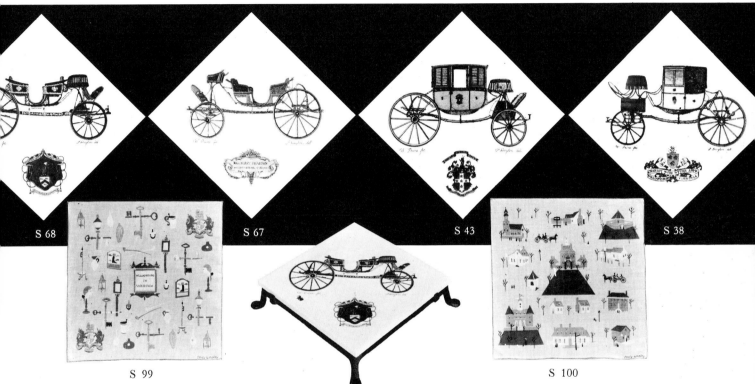

S 68   S 67   S 43   S 38

S 99   S 100

CW 10-42

S 119 Soap Balls. This box of three scented soaps copies the eighteenth-century fashion of forming soap in balls. The scents included are lavender, bayberry, and lemon, and the balls are colored lavender, green, and yellow. Box of three balls (one of each scent) $1.25

S 69 Ash Tray. An engraving of the Governor's Palace decorates this Patrician Shape ash tray by Wedgwood, made especially for Craft House. It is available in sepia, mulberry, or blue on a cream-colored base. Diameter 4½" $2.40

Williamsburg Candles

Bayberry Candles. The spicy aroma of these decorative candles is reminiscent of colonial festivities. Soft green in color, the candles are made by hand in the scullery of the Governor's Palace.

R 4 Small Candles. 10"   Pair $1.80

R 5 Large Candles. Fit CW 16-33 Spiked Candlestick (page 93). 8½"   Pair $4.00

Beeswax Candles. The excellent burning quality of beeswax candles made them very fashionable in the eighteenth century. These candles are made in the Governor's Palace scullery.

R 7 Small Candles. 10"   Pair $1.80

R 8 Large Candles. Fit CW 16-33 Spiked Candlestick (page 93). 8½"   Pair $4.00

Williamsburg Candles (Continued)

S 9 Large White Candles. Fit CW 16-33 Spiked Candlestick (page 93). 10"   Pair $1.80

Williamsburg Carriage Tiles. The colored illustrations of carriages on these tiles were done in the manner of eighteenth-century engravings. 6" x 6"   Each $1.90 Set of 4 $6.05

S 68 Tucker Phaeton   S 43 Randolph Coach
S 67 Mulberry Phaeton   S 38 Wythe Chariot

CW 10-42 Trivet. Any Williamsburg tile will fit this black iron trivet stand. It is illustrated holding a Tucker Phaeton Tile. When ordering, please specify which tile is desired.

          With one Carriage Tile $3.35
          With one Military Tile   4.60
          With one Scenic Tile   3.10

Williamsburg Handkerchiefs

S 99 Williamsburg Handkerchief. Signs and symbols of Williamsburg decorate this fine linen handkerchief. It is available in gray, blue, brown, or yellow.   Each $1.10 Set of 4 $4.25

S 100 Governor's Palace Handkerchief. A view of the Governor's Palace is surrounded by stylized drawings of other Williamsburg buildings on this charming linen handkerchief.   Each $1.10 Set of 4 $4.25

WILLIAMSBURG PENCIL SKETCH NOTES. Scenes of Williamsburg and the surrounding historic area decorate this selection of note papers by Charles Overly. Envelopes are included with each package of notes.

S 16 Twelve different sketches of Williamsburg's buildings, gardens, and interiors capture the spirit of the restored town. 4″ x 4¾″ $1.20

S 29 Twelve sketches of eight Williamsburg scenes are delightful reminders of a visit to the colonial capital. 3½″ x 4½″ $1.20

S 47 Letterettes for Young Folks. This box of paper for young children is lightly lined for easier writing. Charming drawings of the Palace and Apothecary Shop decorate the notes. Fourteen sheets are included. 6″ x 8¼″ $.95

S 70 Recipe Notes. Williamsburg taverns and kitchens are illustrated on this note paper. An eighteenth-century recipe accompanies each scene. A box includes ten notes. 5½″ x 8¼″ $1.20

S 103 JAMESTOWN, WILLIAMSBURG, YORKTOWN NOTES. Twelve folded notes show views of important scenes in the "historic triangle," from the Jamestown fort and famed Williamsburg buildings to Yorktown's Moore House. 3¾″ x 7¼″ $1.25

L 77 BOOK MARK. This genuine leather book mark is available in brown, black, green, yellow, and other colors. 1½″ x 9¼″ $1.90

POST PAPER. This fine quality stationery was copied from antique letter paper in the archives of Colonial Williamsburg. Its charming package is tied with red ribbon and sealed with wax.

K 136 NOTE PAPER. 30 sheets, 20 envelopes; 5″ x 8″ $1.70

K 135 LETTER PAPER. 24 sheets and envelopes; 8″ x 12″ $3.10

S 33 SKETCH PORTFOLIO. Carefully reproduced from fine drawings by Charles Overly, these four pencil sketches include views of Bruton Parish Church, Wren Building, Capitol, and Governor's Palace. 11½″ x 15″ including margins   Set of 4 $1.80

S 85 FOUR DOCUMENTS OF FREEDOM. Facsimiles on antiqued parchment paper of four historic American documents are available for study and for framing. They are the Virginia Resolution for Independence, Virginia Declaration of Rights, Declaration of Independence, and federal Bill of Rights. 13¾″ x 15⅝″   Set of 4 $1.10

S 85

S 70

L 77

K 135

K 136

S 16

S 47

S 29

S 33   S 103

S 107

S 108

William and Mary Ash Trays

The portraits of King William III and Queen Mary II that decorate these Wedgwood ash trays were taken from eighteenth-century engravings attributed to Gaspar de Hollander, a publisher in Antwerp. A pair of these ash trays is an unusually fine gift for a modest price. Diameter 6¼″

S 107 KING WILLIAM ASH TRAY   Pair $5.45
S 108 QUEEN MARY ASH TRAY

Watercolor Prints by Kenneth Harris

The well-known Virginia artist, Kenneth Harris, painted the originals from which these fine prints were taken. Mr. Harris is a member of the American Watercolor Society, and has exhibited his work in more than 50 museums and galleries from New York to Texas. The pleasing colors and meticulous detail of these delightful scenes make them treasured mementoes of a Williamsburg visit.

P 17

P 16

P 16 WREN BUILDING
    Unframed, 25¾″ x 18⅞″ including margins $5.30
    Framed in mahogany and gold leaf, 28″ x 21″ $30.50

P 17 BRUTON PARISH CHURCH
    Unframed, 25¾″ x 18⅞″ including margins $5.30
    Framed in mahogany and gold leaf, 28″ x 21″ $30.50

P 18 ALONG DUKE OF GLOUCESTER STREET
    Unframed, 34½″ x 25½″ including margins $12.60
    Framed in mahogany and gold leaf, 27¾″ x 37″ $54.50

P 18

S 50

S 40

S 114/115

S 109

PLAYING CARDS. One of these decks has an exterior view of the Capitol in Williamsburg; the other a view of the Governor's Palace.

S 157 SINGLE DECK	Specify Design	$1.15
S 50 DOUBLE DECK		$2.00
S 111 TRIPLE DECK	Specify Design	$2.90

S 40 BRIDGE PACK. Scenes of Williamsburg decorate this set of three score pads and twelve tallies. $1.40

S 114/115 COLONIAL CURRENCY. Accurately reproduced on antiqued paper, this facsimile money includes samples of paper currency from each of the thirteen original colonies. It is packaged in two envelopes.

Set of two envelopes. $.60

S 109 THE GREAT GAME OF VISITING WILLIAMSBURG. Suitable for ages 7 to 12, this exciting game takes the children on a tour of historic Williamsburg. They learn history while they play. $3.05

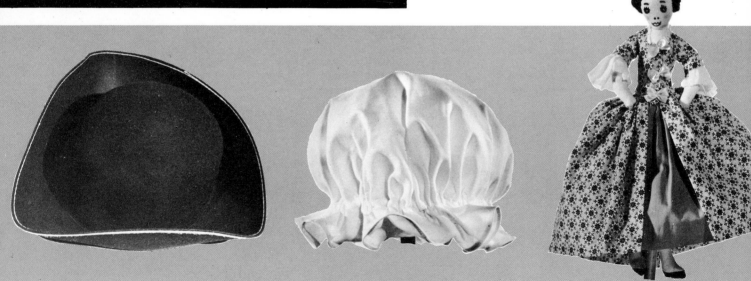

S 46 TRICORN HAT. This hat, made of black wool trimmed with gold-colored braid, was inspired by tricorn hats popular in eighteenth-century Williamsburg. It fits youngsters 6-12 years of age. $1.45

S 129 MOBCAP. Patterned after an eighteenth-century headpiece, this white cotton cap delights the young girl and fits any head size. Costumed women in Williamsburg today may be seen wearing this quaint ruffled cap. $1.40

S 133 DOLL. An excellent addition to a doll collection, this handmade stuffed doll is dressed in the style used by Colonial Williamsburg's hostesses. The face is hand-painted. Height 11½" $5.50

TOYS and GAMES

S 131 *Williamsburg* GUN CREW AND SIEGE PIECE. Made of lead and hand-painted in careful detail, these six miniatures include models of a five-man colonial gun crew and an eighteenth-century cannon. Each figure is wearing colonial military garb and is holding a piece of traditional firing equipment, patterned after the antique tools in Williamsburg's Powder Magazine. The set was inspired by the famed Colonial Williamsburg militia, which drills and fires old weapons twice weekly in Williamsburg. $7.75

S 134 *Williamsburg* CHECKER SET. Reproduced from an antique set in the Colonial Williamsburg collection, each piece of this unusual checker set is decorated with an illustration from Aesop's fables. The pieces are made of composition resembling wood, and the playing board is on the outside of the box in the manner of antique game chests. The original from which this handsome set was copied was probably made in England in the eighteenth century.
Board 18½″ x 19″ $16.25
S 134-B Checkers only $9.55

Williamsburg MUSIC SHEETS. Each of these packets of songs contains six facsimile reproductions of eighteenth-century music taken from George Bickham's *Musical Entertainer*, published in London in 1738. The charming melodies may be performed on modern musical instruments, and the gracefully illustrated sheets may be framed for hanging in library or music room. 10½″ x 16½″
  Songs of Politics and Potation $1.40
  Songs of Gentility $1.40

BROOMS

R 3 HEARTH BROOM. This reproduction of a colonial broom is useful and charming on the hearth. It is made of undressed broom straw. Length 26″ $2.45

S 1 DOLL BROOM. An unusual accessory, this hand-made Mammy broom is a cheerful addition to the fireplace. Length 32″
  Discontinued

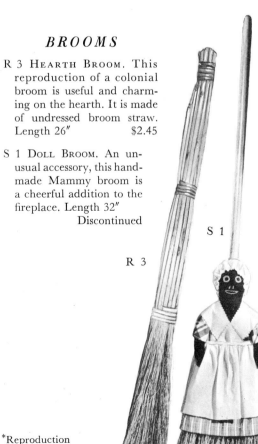

R 3

S 1

*Reproduction

S 131

S 134

E

Music Sheets

Colonial Williamsburg Publications

THE PAGES OF HISTORY literally unfold as you browse through the Williamsburg books published by Colonial Williamsburg. As an integral part of its educational program, Colonial Williamsburg has developed an expanding publications program that includes books of scholarship, popular histories, books styled after the fashion of the eighteenth century, books on contemporary Williamsburg, and books for children. All Colonial Williamsburg publications may be obtained at Craft House, which also offers a wide selection of Williamsburg books of other publishers.

Children's Books

ADVENTURE IN WILLIAMSBURG, photographs by Carroll Seghers II, text by John J. Walklet, Jr. The delightful photographic story of the adventures of two children in restored Williamsburg. All ages. 48 pages. Cloth binding. $1.15

AMERICA'S FIRST ARMY by Burke Davis; illustrated by Richard J. Stinely; photographs by John Crane. With 7-inch, 33⅓ rpm L.P. record of today's Williamsburg militia muster. Paper. $2.10

PIRATE CHASE by Earl Schenck Miers; illustrated by Peter Burchard. Exciting times when young Tim Baillie on his way from Williamsburg to England is captured by the terrible Blackbeard. His subsequent adventures provide a stirring climax. Ages 9 to 12. 129 pages. Paper over boards. $4.10

PROUD PRISONER by Walter Havighurst; illustrated by Leonard Vosburgh. The story of Lieutenant Governor Henry Hamilton, British commander of strategic Detroit, whom Americans called the "Hair Buyer." Ages 12 to 16. 140 pages. Paper over boards. $4.10

REBEL'S ROOST by Earl Schenck Miers; illustrated by Fritz Kredel. A book that captures the human spirit of old Williamsburg in those stirring times when ideals of individual liberty and national union were struggling to be born. Ages 12 to 16. 148 pages. Cloth binding. $2.90

THE BELOVED FRIEND by Marguerite Vance; illustrated by Leonard Weisgard. The poignant story of Sally Cary Fairfax and her lifelong friend, George Washington. Ages 12 to 16. 120 pages. Cloth binding. $4.10

THE FRENCH ARE COMING by Wilma Pitchford Hays; illustrated by Leonard Weisgard. An exciting story of how the French came to Virginia and helped defeat the British regulars at Yorktown in the decisive battle of the American Revolution. Ages 8 to 12. 120 pages. Paper over boards. $4.10

THE SCARLET BADGE by Wilma Pitchford Hays; illustrated by Peter Burchard. The tale of Rob Roberts, caught between loyalty to his king and love for his native land. Ages 11 to 14. 109 pages. Paper over boards. $4.10

TO THE WALLS OF CARTAGENA by Allan Dwight; illustrated by Leonard Vosburgh. This story of spies and scoundrels, of buccaneers and booty, of legendary lost treasure, and of the courage, resolution, and loyalty of sixteen-year-old Greg Shelby is set in 1739 against the background of the War of Jenkins' Ear. Ages 10 to 14. 176 pages. Paper over boards. $4.10

TOMAHAWK BORDER by William O. Steele; illustrated by Vernon Wooten. In 1714 on the southwestern frontier of Virginia, young Delk Rogers joins the rangers and earns first criticism and finally acceptance by them. Ages 10 to 14. 129 pages. Paper over boards. $4.10

WAYAH OF THE REAL PEOPLE by William O. Steele; illustrated by Isa Barnett. Life at Brafferton Hall, the Indian school at the College of William and Mary, as seen through the eyes of a Cherokee Indian boy. Ages 10 to 14. 138 pages. Paper over boards. $4.10

BRAVE HORSE by Manly Wade Wellman; illustrated by Peter Burchard. The story of the gallant Janus, who was disabled and retired from the English track, yet who lived to challenge William Byrd's Valiant, the finest racehorse in the colony of Virginia, and who became the foundation sire of the American quarter horse. Ages 10 to 14. 118 pages. Paper over boards. $4.10

MARY'S STAR by Wilma Pitchford Hays; illustrated by Lawrence Beall Smith. A tale of three orphans in Virginia near the close of the Revolutionary War—Mary Breckenridge, whose father was killed in battle; Deke Lester, her father's blacksmith apprentice; and Star, the young colt who helped Mary and Deke accept the changes wrought in their lives. Ages 10 to 14. 108 pages. Paper over boards. $4.10

Williamsburg Today

COLONIAL WILLIAMSBURG: ITS BUILDINGS AND GARDENS, Revised Edition by A. Lawrence Kocher and Howard Dearstyne. Photographs by Herbert Matter and Thomas L. Williams. A distinctive interpretation by distinguished architects of Colonial Williamsburg. 112 pages. Cloth binding. $5.10

COLONIAL WILLIAMSBURG OFFICIAL GUIDEBOOK AND MAP. Here is Colonial Williamsburg, street by street, house by house, with the intimate story of each building and shop in terms of the people who lived and worked in eighteenth-century Williamsburg. Illustrated. Large color map. 126 pages. Paper binding. $.65

A WINDOW ON WILLIAMSBURG, photographs by Taylor Biggs Lewis, Jr.; text by John J. Walklet, Jr. An intimate glimpse of Virginia's restored eighteenth-century capital in 110 full-color photographs. 72 pages. Paper binding, $2.10; paper over boards, $4.10

History

A WILLIAMSBURG GALAXY by Burke Davis; illustrated. While it was the seat of empire for the largest British colony in North America, Williamsburg drew all men to it—those who built it and those who were molded by it, from Governor Francis Nicholson to Governor Thomas Jefferson. They came to Williamsburg, both the British and the native sons, and after they had been there neither they, nor the town, nor the history of America was ever again the same. 232 pages. Paper over boards. $5.10

A WILLIAMSBURG SONGBOOK by John Edmunds; illustrated by Fritz Kredel. Being songs convivial, sporting, amorous, etc., from eighteenth-century collections known to have been in the libraries of colonial Virginians. 152 pages. Marbled paper over boards. $6.10

ALEXANDER SPOTSWOOD: Portrait of a Governor by Walter Havighurst. Governor of the royal colony of Virginia from 1710 to 1722, Alexander Spotswood, ambitious and resolute, left his mark on the colony and on Williamsburg, its capital. 144 pages. Paper over boards. $4.10

BLOOD OF FREEDOM by Earl Schenck Miers; illustrated by Richard J. Stinely. The story of the British colonists in North America from Jamestown to Yorktown. In this book, Mr. Miers traces with imagination and sensitivity an epic unsurpassed in American history. Cloth binding. 192 pages. $5.10

GEORGE MASON, RELUCTANT STATESMAN by Robert A. Rutland. A biography in brief of Virginia's eighteenth-century champion of the individual and author of the Virginia Declaration of Rights. Illustrated. 144 pages. Cloth binding. $3.65

SEAT OF EMPIRE by Carl Bridenbaugh. The story of why Williamsburg, commercially of little significance, ranked as the political and social peer of other colonial capitals. Illustrated. 96 pages. $4.10

SONGS FROM A COLONIAL TAVERN by Tayler Vrooman; illustrated by Richard J. Stinely. For medium voice and piano, with chords for guitar. 23 songs of colonial days. 48 pages. Paper binding. $2.90

THE EIGHTEENTH-CENTURY HOUSES OF WILLIAMSBURG by Marcus Whiffen. An architectural history of the most important and interesting houses in Williamsburg. Includes descriptions of the George Wythe, Brush-Everard, St. George Tucker, Coke-Garrett houses among many others. 244 pages. Cloth binding. $10.15

THE JOURNAL AND LETTERS OF PHILIP VICKERS FITHIAN edited by Hunter Dickinson Farish; illustrated by Fritz Kredel. A lively, informal glimpse of plantation life as recorded by a tutor in the household of Robert Carter of Nomini Hall. 304 pages. Cloth binding. $4.10

THE JOURNAL OF JOHN HARROWER edited by Edward Miles Riley; illustrated by Fritz Kredel. This unique journal of an indentured servant living in the colony of Virginia from 1773-1776 presents a lively and detailed picture of plantation life on the eve of the Revolution. 202 pages. Cloth binding. $4.10

THE JOURNAL OF MAJOR GEORGE WASHINGTON edited by James R. Short and Thaddeus W. Tate, Jr. An account of Washington's first official mission, at the age of 21, to the commandant of the French forces on the Ohio; October 1753 to January 1754. A facsimile edition. 60 pages. $2.15

THE PUBLIC BUILDINGS OF WILLIAMSBURG by Marcus Whiffen. An architectural history and study of some of the most significant and influential buildings in colonial America. 286 pages. Cloth binding. $12.65

VIRGINIANS AT HOME by Edmund Morgan. The day-to-day life of eighteenth-century Virginians is presented with an easy informality. Pictured for you are: a school boy, a bride, a master, slaves, and holidays. Illustrated. 112 pages. Cloth binding. $2.90

WILLIAMSBURG IN VIRGINIA by Rutherfoord Goodwin. An official history of Williamsburg. ". . . Being an Account of the most important Occurrences in that Place from its first Beginning to the present Time." Eighteenth-century typography and illustrations. 428 pages. Marbled paper over boards. $6.10

Williamsburg Research Studies

BOOKBINDING IN COLONIAL VIRGINIA by C. Clement Samford and John M. Hemphill II. A two-fold account of this colonial craft: a history drawn from the remaining eighteenth-century records and an analysis of the technique based on an examination of books bound in Annapolis, Williamsburg, and Richmond. Illustrated with photographs of bindings and rubs and details of bindings. 209 pages. Paper-bound. $4.15

COLONIAL VIRGINIANS AT PLAY by Jane Carson. A compilation and interpretation of source materials dealing with sports and amusements in the Virginia colony, including manuscripts and printed diaries, letters, account books, orders, inventories, official records, and newspapers. Illustrated with photographs of contemporary prints, toys, and game equipment. 342 pages. Paper-bound. $3.50

CRIMINAL TRIAL PROCEEDINGS IN THE GENERAL COURT OF COLONIAL VIRGINIA by Hugh F. Rankin. A history of the General Court and an analysis of its organization and procedure in the eighteenth century, based on the only extant records; for this reason, emphasis is on criminal trials. 248 pages. Paper-bound. $3.00

JAMES INNES AND HIS BROTHERS OF THE F. H. C. by Jane Carson. Historical notes on the first college fraternity in British America, the F. H. C. Society of the College of William and Mary, and a biographical sketch of one of its members, Col. James Innes (1754-98), a typical Virginia patriot. 182 pages. Paper-bound. $2.25

THE NEGRO IN EIGHTEENTH-CENTURY WILLIAMSBURG by Thad W. Tate, Jr. An interpretation of the impact of town life on an element in the population whose prime function in Virginia was the performance of agricultural labor. 270 pages. Paper-bound. $3.00

TRAVELERS IN TIDEWATER VIRGINIA, 1700-1800: A bibliography by Jane Carson. An alphabetical listing of written records of personal visits to be found in books, pamphlets, periodicals, and manuscript collections; annotations are restricted to the Virginia portions of the visit and the author's point of view and reliability. 136 pages. Paper-bound. $2.00

THE ECONOMIC ROLE OF WILLIAMSBURG by James H. Soltow. Since Williamsburg was not an important port town, this study emphasizes the periodic Meetings of Merchants, especially in regard to the setting of the exchange rate with Great Britain. 240 pages. Paper-bound. $3.00

WE WERE THERE: Descriptions of Williamsburg, 1699-1859 by Jane Carson. A compilation of descriptions of the town at the time of each author's visit, arranged chronologically, with a complete bibliographical citation and brief note about the author—the extent of his travels, his interest, and point of view. 140 pages. Paper-bound. $2.00

COLONIAL VIRGINIA COOKERY by Jane Carson. Not a cookbook *per se* but a book about cookery—how the colonial housewife met meal-planning challenges without neighborhood food stores, refrigeration, canning, reliable equipment, or standard measures. The colonial kitchen, its equipment and utensils, is described in detail, and selected recipes from eighteenth-century cookbooks are included. 212 pages. Paper-bound. $4.15

Miscellaneous Titles

PLANTS OF COLONIAL DAYS by Raymond L. Taylor. A guide to 160 flowers, trees, and shrubs in the gardens of Colonial Williamsburg. 112 pages. Paper binding. $1.65

THE ABBY ALDRICH ROCKEFELLER FOLK ART COLLECTION by Nina Fletcher Little. A descriptive catalogue in magnificent full color of one of the world's outstanding collections of American folk art. 165 color reproductions. 420 pages. Hand-marbled paper over boards. $9.15

THE FLOWER WORLD OF WILLIAMSBURG by Joan Parry Dutton; photographs in color and black-and-white. Traces the development of eighteenth-century gardens and styles of flower arranging. 160 pages. Paper over boards. $5.10

THE WILLIAMSBURG ART OF COOKERY by Helen Bullock. A tempting collection of "upwards of Five Hundred of the most Ancient and Approv'd Recipes in *Virginia* Cookery." 306 pages. Leather binding $6.65; paper over boards $3.65

Articles in this catalogue have been approved by Williamsburg Restoration, Incorporated

LICENSED MANUFACTURERS

Brass and Iron Accessories
Virginia Metalcrafters, Incorporated
Waynesboro, Virginia 22980

Clocks
Chelsea Clock Company
284 Everett Avenue
Chelsea, Massachusetts 02150

Delft
Foreign Advisory Service Corp.
Princess Anne, Maryland 21853

Messrs. Oud Delft of Nijmegen,
Holland

Dinnerware and Ceramics
Josiah Wedgwood & Sons, Inc.
24 East 54th Street
New York, New York 10022

Fabrics
F. Schumacher & Company
58 West 40th Street
New York, New York 10018

Figurines and Character Jugs
Doulton & Company, Incorporated
11 East 26th Street
New York, New York 10010

Fireplace Equipment
The Harvin Company
Waynesboro, Virginia 22980

Furniture
Kittinger Company, Incorporated
1893 Elmwood Avenue
Buffalo, New York 14207

Glass
Foreign Advisory Service Corp.
Princess Anne, Maryland 21853

Royal Leerdam, Leerdam, Holland

Lamp Accessories
Knob Creek of Morganton
Morganton, North Carolina 28655

Leather
Lackawanna Leather Company
Hackettstown, New Jersey 07840

Lighting Fixtures
Virginia Metalcrafters, Incorporated
Waynesboro, Virginia 22980

Locks
Folger Adam Company
P. O. Box 1148
Joliet, Illinois 60434

Mirrors
Friedman Brothers Decorative Arts,
Incorporated
305 East 47th Street
New York, New York 10017

Needle Point & Needlework
Paragon Art and Linen Co., Inc.
385 Fifth Avenue
New York, New York 10016

Paint
Martin-Senour Paints
2500 South Senour Avenue
Chicago, Illinois 60608

Pewter and Silver
The Stieff Company
Wyman Park Driveway
Baltimore, Maryland 21211

Pottery
Williamsburg Pottery
Rt. 3, Box 148
Williamsburg, Virginia 23185

Prints
The Dietz Press, Incorporated
109 East Cary Street
Richmond, Virginia 23219

Stationery
Eaton Paper Corporation
Pittsfield, Massachusetts 01203

Wallpaper
Katzenbach & Warren, Incorporated
575 Madison Avenue
New York, New York 10022

Wooden Accessories
Victorius, Incorporated
1313 Belleview Avenue
Charlottesville, Virginia 22902

OTHER MANUFACTURERS

Correspondence Notes
Charles Overly
Old Littleton Road
Harvard, Massachusetts 01451

Dried Flowers
18th Century Bouquet, Incorporated
53 State Road
Princeton, New Jersey 08540

Soap
Carolina Soap and Candlemakers
Southern Pines, North Carolina
28387

DIRECTIONS FOR ORDERING

An order blank and a postage-saver envelope are enclosed for your convenience. Please furnish your name and address (including Zip Code Number), as well as catalogue number and description of articles ordered.

A Supplemental Price List is enclosed.

All prices quoted include shipping charges by usual methods. Special delivery or air mail charges will be extra.

Craft House sells at retail only.

Special prices for sets or pairs (as quoted) are for shipment to one address.

Safe delivery of shipments is guaranteed. In case of damage, please notify Craft House without delay.

If you do not have a Craft House Charge Account Number enclose a check (payable to Craft House) for the total amount of purchase. If you wish to open a Charge Account an application will be sent upon request.

To order by telephone, call Area Code 703, 229-1000 between 9:00 A.M. and 5:00 P.M. Monday through Saturday.

Craft House will gladly forward gifts directly to your friends. Enclose your card with the order, furnishing name and address (including Zip Code Number) of the recipient.

PRICES SUBJECT TO CHANGE WITHOUT NOTICE

MARTIN
SENOUR
PAINTS

THE MARTIN-SENOUR COMPANY
IS HONORED TO HAVE BEEN
OFFICIALLY CHOSEN TO
REPRODUCE THE AUTHENTIC
PAINT COLORS OF
COLONIAL WILLIAMSBURG.

THE HISTORY AND ROMANCE
OF COLONIAL AMERICA
CAN BE YOURS WITH THESE
HANDSOME AND EASY TO APPLY
INTERIOR AND EXTERIOR PAINTS

Williamsburg®

BRACKEN HOUSE BISCUIT
W1064

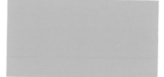

GRIFFIN HOUSE IVORY
W1073

BRACKEN HOUSE BLUE SLATE
W1065

ARCHIBALD BLAIR GREEN
W1061

PITT-DIXON GREEN
W1088

MOIR SHOP FAWN
W1080

CARTER-SAUNDERS TOBACCO
W1069

LUDWELL TENEMENT SAGE*
W1079

POWELL-WALLER HOUSE GREEN
W1089

BRUSH-EVERARD GOLD
W1067

PALACE ARMS RED
W1083

BARRAUD HOUSE GREEN
W1062

PALMER HOUSE GREEN
W1084

ARCHIBALD BLAIR GOLD
W1060

NICOLSON SHOP RED
W1081

GOVERNOR'S PALACE TAN
W1072

JAMES GEDDY GREEN
W1075

LUDWELL TENEMENT GOLD*
W1078

BRACKEN HOUSE BROWN
W1066

HOLT'S STOREHOUSE GRAY
W1074

LEVINGSTON KITCHEN GREEN*
W1077

PITT-DIXON CARAMEL
W1087

PALMER HOUSE KITCHEN BROWN*
W1085

PEYTON RANDOLPH GRAY
W1086

DRAPER HOUSE GREEN
W1071

NICOLSON SHOP TAUPE
W1082

BRYAN HOUSE CHOCOLATE
W1068

KING'S ARMS TAVERN GRAY
W1076

BLAIR HOUSE GREEN
W1063

RALEIGH TAVERN SORREL
W1091

CHOWNING'S TAVERN BROWN
W1070

PURDIE HOUSE GRAY SLATE
W1090

TALIAFERRO-COLE BLACK GREEN
W1092

*See copy.

nterior

This sample shows sheen of satin gloss enamel.

	MEDIUM	MEDIUM LIGHT	LIGHT

T SQUARE GREEN — W1031, W1032, W1033, W1034

E BALLROOM BLUE — W1035, W1036, W1037, W1038

ARMS ROSE PINK — W1027, W1028, •W1029, •W1030

NIAL GREEN — W1023, W1024, W1025, •W1026

E HOUSE GOLD — W1055, W1056, W1057, •W1058

NING'S TAVERN ROSE TAN — W1019, W1020, W1021, W1022

GH TAVERN TAN — W1051, W1052, •W1053, •W1054

AM GRAY — W1039, W1040, W1041, W1042

GH TAVERN PEACH — W1047, W1048, •W1049, •W1050

LO ROOM BLUE — W1011, W1012, W1013, W1014

HECARY SHOP BLUE — W1015, W1016, W1017, W1018

GH TAVERN GREEN — W1043, W1044, W1045, W1046

• AVAILABLE IN GALLONS ONLY

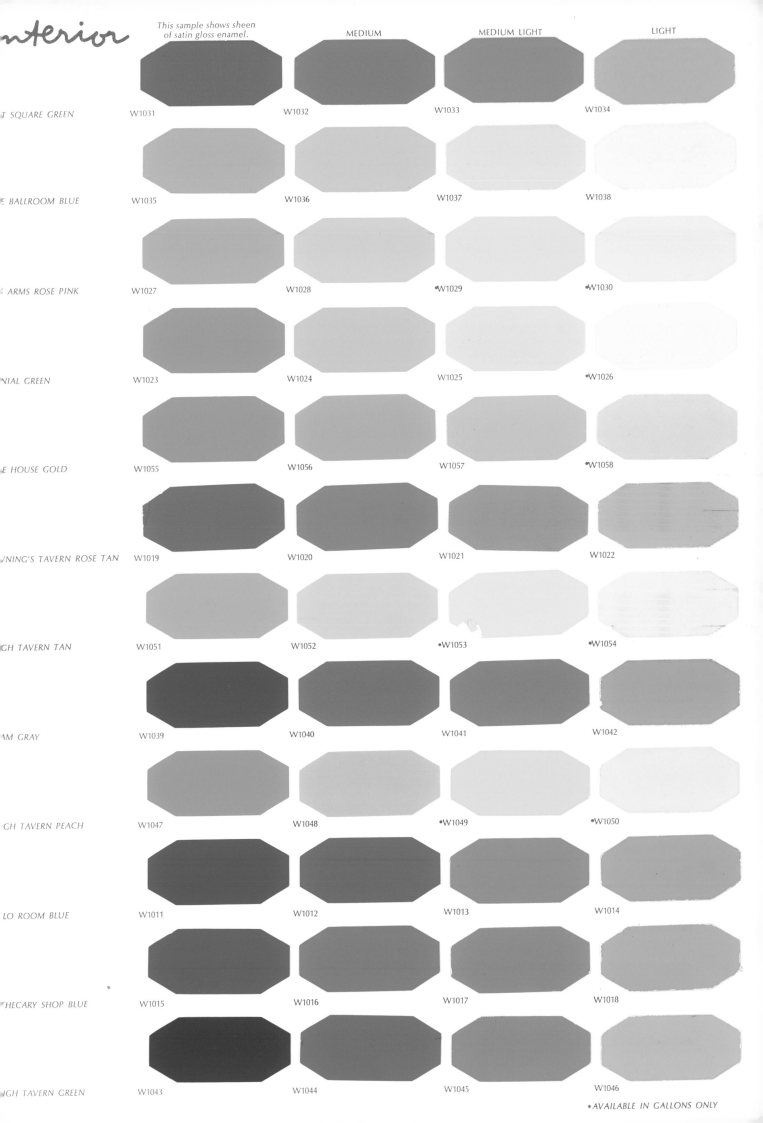

HISTORY

Williamsburg, founded more than two hundred years ago, was destined to become the capitol of His Majesty's crown colony of Virginia, and the training ground for leaders of American independence. Here George Washington, Patrick Henry, Thomas Jefferson, and other patriots helped shape the foundations of our government.

In 1926 Mr. John D. Rockefeller, Jr. became interested in the preservation and restoration of Williamsburg. This work has continued and today the Historic Area of Colonial Williamsburg embraces 130 acres. Within this area, there are nearly one hundred original Eighteenth Century homes and shops. Ninety acres of colorful gardens and greens have been re-created using only plants known to Eighteenth Century colonists.

Paint was widely used in Colonial Williamsburg and here the visitor can see the homes and shops restored to their original colors—many of which are reproduced on this color card.

HISTORIAN-DETECTIVES

When a group of historian-detectives began the work of rebuilding, duplicating the original paint colors was one of their major problems. The old houses had been repainted many times. Often a careful scraping and minute examination of the particles was necessary before the character of the original paint was revealed. Other times the old paint could be discovered amazingly fresh and bright behind cornices and in dark closets, or beneath two centuries of paint and wallpaper. In other cases, it might be made up from a "recipe" mentioned in a directive to painters or from a list of materials in old letters ordering such exotic ingredients as copperas, fish oil, lamp black, Spanish brown, verdigris, and indigo.

TREND SETTING COLORS

As these diligent researchers revealed the original colors they found those enjoyed by the great statesman Thomas Jefferson as well as the humble milliner Margaret Hunter. Perhaps they didn't realize that also they were setting new contemporary standards of color for interior decoration. The selection of soft, rich WILLIAMSBURG interior colors reflected one aspect of Colonial society that the Twentieth Century eagerly embraced. WILLIAMSBURG colors are now firmly established in the American decorating tradition.

NOW EXTERIOR!

The variety of exterior colors to be seen in Williamsburg never fails to surprise the visitor. Some houses show as many as five different colors on the exteriors. The color combinations are fresh and new. Some seem almost contemporary. New exterior color discoveries are being made every year.

Now, for the first time, Martin Senour presents a palette of these appealing colors. It is expected that these newly revealed but authentic colors from America's early history will have the same impact on exterior color styling that the interior colors have had on interior decoration.

WILLIAMSBURG HALLMARK

Your seal of authenticity is the WILLIAMSBURG Hallmark. No other paints have been matched to the specimens in Williamsburg and approved by Williamsburg Restoration, Incorporated. Look for the WILLIAMSBURG Hallmark. It alone identifies genuine WILLIAMSBURG Paints made exclusively by Martin Senour.

MARTIN SENOUR QUALITY

WILIAMSBURG Colors are the finest paints available today. They are manufactured to meet the highest standards of quality and performance. Ready-mixed, easy to apply, they have excellent hiding power and dry to a beautiful, durable finish. WILLIAMSBURG Colors stay bright and new-looking longer because of pigments with superior permanence.

---

*Meaning of the word "tenement" has changed since Colonial days when it simply meant "rental property." Such extra living quarters were in demand, particularly during sessions of the House of Burgesses when delegates assembled in Williamsburg for many months at a time.

*The kitchen in Old Williamsburg usually was a separate building. This kept the fire hazard of open-hearth cooking away from the dwelling.

Along with other outbuildings, the kitchen sometimes was painted a color different from the house. Levingston Kitchen Green and Palmer House Kitchen Brown are two such colors.

INTERIOR ALKYD FLAT

Application: Easily applied by brush, roller or spray.

Surfaces: All interior wall areas.

Preparation: Over previously painted surfaces in good condition, this product generally covers in one coat. When a second coat is required, allow ample drying time (overnight) before recoating. For new work, a first coat of Martin Senour Primer and Sealer (#348) or Quik-Sealer (#2646) is recommended. Allow for ample time to dry then follow with finish coat of Alkyd Flat.

Drying Time: This finish dries to touch in 1 to 2 hours and is hard in 10 to 12 hours.

INTERIOR SATIN GLOSS

Application: Easily applied by brush, roller or spray.

Surfaces: Interior wall and trim areas also cabinets and furniture.

Preparation: Covers most surfaces in one coat. Where a second coat is required, allow ample drying time (overnight) between coats. For new work, apply a prime coat or undercoat tinted to approximate the finish color. Allow ample time to dry and finish with Satin Gloss Enamel.

Drying Time: Dries to touch in 4 hours and is hard in 10 to 12 hours.

EXTERIOR GLOSS HOUSE PAINT

Application: May be brushed or sprayed.

Surfaces: Exterior use over wood and metal. The deep accent colors are excellent for doors, shutters, and window sashes.

Preparation: Over previously painted surfaces in good condition, with *minimum color* difference, one coat applied at full body will usually suffice. If, however, there is *considerable color difference*, two finish coats may be necessary. Over new wood or badly weathered surfaces, apply a first coat of tinted Monarch 350 Undercoat. Allow for thorough dry and then apply a finish coat of Williamsburg Exterior Gloss House Paint.

Drying Time: Normally, WILLIAMSBURG Exterior Paints will dry overnight. Allow 3 to 4 days for drying between coats.

Coverage: One gallon will cover approximately 450 to 550 square feet.

COLORS APPROVED BY WILLIAMSBURG RESTORATION INCORPORATED. MADE BY THE MARTIN-SENOUR COMPANY UNDER LICENSE FROM WILLIAMSBURG RESTORATION, INC., OWNER OF THE TRADEMARKS

Williamsburg

AND THE HALLMARK REG. U.S. PAT. OFF.

MARTIN SENOUR PAINTS • 2500 SOUTH SENOUR AVENUE • CHICAGO 60608